845· 399·5491

The Association of International
Photography Art Dealers

The Photography Show 2007

April 12 - April 15

Membership Directory
& Illustrated Catalogue

D1262618

The Association of International Photography Art Dealers [AIPAD]
1767 P Street, NW, Second Floor
Washington, DC 20036
tel: 202-986-0105
fax: 202-986-0448
e-mail: info@aipad.com
web: www.aipad.com
Membership Directory & Illustrated Catalogue © 2007 AIPAD

Membership Directory & Illustrated Catalogue

Show Production, Kathleen Ewing

Catalogue Production, Lizzy Evelyn

Production Assistants, Charlotte Vazquez, Ingrid Yan

Catalogue Advertising & Marketing, Patricia Hoffman

Catalogue Printing, Anaconda Press, Inc.
7908 Parston Drive, Forestville, Maryland 20747
tel: 301-967-2300 / 800-528-9775 / e-mail: aipad@anacondapress.com

The Photography Show 2007 Promotion Design and Catalogue Cover
Lloyd Blander, New York, NY / Web: www.lloydblander.com

$25.00 including postage / $45 outside the U.S. including postage

© 2007 AIPAD 2007 Membership Directory & Illustrated Catalogue
The Photography Show 2007
ISBN: 1-893590-08-9
ISSN: 1554-138X

TABLE OF CONTENTS

THE ASSOCIATION OF INTERNATIONAL PHOTOGRAPHY ART DEALERS, INC.

The Association of International Photography Art Dealers [AIPAD] was organized in 1979. With members in the United States, Australia, Canada, Europe and Japan, the Association has become a unifying force in the field of photography. AIPAD is dedicated to creating and maintaining high standards in the business of exhibiting, buying and selling photographs as art.

Acting as the collective voice of the art photography dealers that make up its membership, AIPAD maintains ethical standards, promotes communication within the photographic community, encourages public appreciation of photography as art, concerns itself with the rights of photographers and collectors, and works to enhance the confidence of the public in responsible photograph dealers. AIPAD members provide a wide range of services to the public, such as exhibitions, appraisals, expert opinions and consultations.

AIPAD Members have agreed to a Code of Ethics: Members agree to conduct dealings with the public, museums, artists and other dealers with honesty and integrity. Members agree to provide accurate descriptions of photographs in all disclosures, including but not limited to, invoices, wall labels and price lists. All descriptions shall include the following: (1) Artist, (2) Title / Subject, (3) Process, (4) Date of negative, (5) Date of print, (6) Price. Members agree to honor all contracts, invoices and consignment agreements.

To qualify for membership in AIPAD, a gallery or dealer must meet a number of criteria. The applicant must demonstrate that a significant portion of his principal business has been and is devoted to the sale and promotion of fine art photographs which meet the Association's high artistic standards. The potential member must have a reputation in his community for honesty and integrity. The potential member must demonstrate that he has made and is making substantial contributions to the field of fine art photography through the quality of photographic art offered for sale, exhibitions mounted or catalogues published. A potential member must have met these criteria for at least five years and be sponsored by five current members of AIPAD.

PRESIDENT'S STATEMENT

I am pleased to welcome you to the Park Avenue Armory and AIPAD's 27th annual exposition of fine photography: **THE PHOTOGRAPHY SHOW 2007**.

This longevity distinguishes our show as the longest running and most prestigious exposition in the world dedicated to photography as fine art.

AIPAD members were the first art dealers to appreciate the artistic value of photography. As leaders in the fine art photography industry, AIPAD's dealers have the depth of knowledge to present the finest vintage works, possess a perspective to discern originality in contemporary photography, and have the experience to understand the value of new technology. THE PHOTOGRAPHY SHOW is a great resource for those interested in collecting photography at all levels. You will find an exciting, collaborative spirit to this event where curators, collectors and people with a fresh interest in photography join to look and learn from the world's leading photography dealers.

By choosing to schedule THE PHOTOGRAPHY SHOW in April, AIPAD is taking an initial step in a long a range plan to create a month-long celebration of photography in New York where auctions, museum shows, lectures and exhibitions inspire a deeper appreciation of fine photography.

Unlike other photography fairs, exhibitors at THE PHOTOGRAPHY SHOW are exclusively AIPAD members. In order to qualify for membership applicants must demonstrate that, for a minimum of five years, they have been committed to the highest standards of exhibiting and promoting photography as a fine art. In addition, exhibitors at THE PHOTOGRAPHY SHOW are reviewed by the Show Committee to ensure that their presentation meets AIPAD's high standards. Visitors to THE PHOTOGRAPHY SHOW can expect to find the very best quality in the field of fine art photography.

This year AIPAD is proud to host an opening night benefit honoring the efforts of the collector and humanitarian, Henry Buhl. The Association of Community Employment Programs for the Homeless (A.C.E.), and it's local initiatives, The SoHo and TriBeCa Partnerships, founded by Henry Buhl, helps homeless men and women rebuild their lives and achieve self-sufficiency through job training programs.

In keeping with AIPAD's commitment to education, we invite you to attend the free presentation about Henry Buhl's renowned collection of photographs of hands titled: "The Passionate Eye: Henry Buhl, Collector, in Conversation with Jennifer Blessing, Curator of Photography, Guggenheim Museum" on Saturday, April 14, 10-11am in the Peter B. Lewis Theater at the Guggenheim Museum.

AIPAD takes great pride in the publication of this annual Membership Directory and Illustrated Catalogue which is included with admission to THE PHOTOGRAPHY SHOW. With its extensive list of photographers and dealers, AIPAD's annual catalogue has proven to be a uniquely valuable tool for curators, collectors, and anyone interested in fine art photography. The catalogue is available throughout the year by contacting the AIPAD offices.

On behalf of AIPAD's Board of Directors and the AIPAD members, I extend a warm welcome and wish you a rewarding visit to **THE PHOTOGRAPHY SHOW 2007**.

Robert L. Klein
President, AIPAD

THE PHOTOGRAPHY SHOW 2007 EXHIBITORS LIST AND FLOOR PLAN

PARK AVENUE ARMORY, PARK AVENUE AND 67TH STREET
NEW YORK, NEW YORK

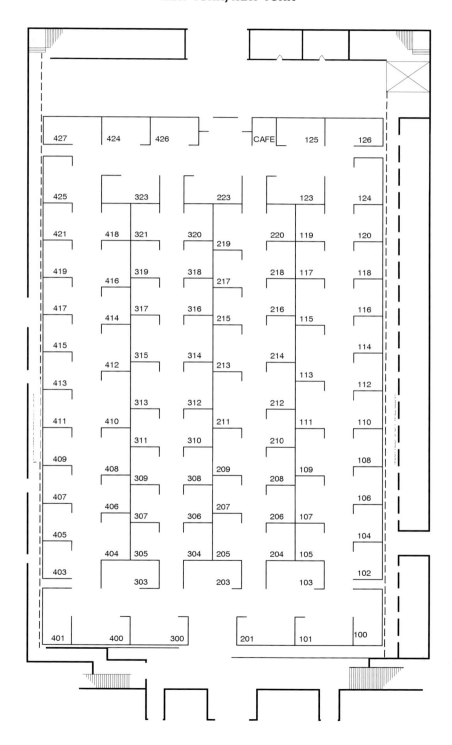

2007 AIPAD MEMBERSHIP

A Gallery for Fine Photography
241 Chartres Street
New Orleans, LA 70130
tel: 504-568-1313
fax: 504-568-1322
e-mail: joshuamann@att.net
web: www.agallery.com
Joshua Mann Pailet, Chief
Edward Hébert, Director

A.P.H. - Christian Bouqueret
21, rue Beaurepaire
Paris, 75010, France
tel/fax: 33-1-40-03-02-73
e-mail: aph.bouqueret@free.fr
Christian Bouqueret, Director
Eric Remy, Assistant

Afterimage Gallery
Quadrangle #141
2800 Routh Street
Dallas, TX 75201
tel: 214-871-9140
fax: 801-858-5282
e-mail: images@afterimagegallery.com
web: www.afterimage.com
Ben Breard, Owner/Director

Nailya Alexander Gallery
24 West 57th Street, #503
New York, NY 10019
tel: 212-315-2211
fax: 212-315-2220
e-mail: nailya@mindspring.com
web: www.nailyaalexandergallery.com
Nailya Alexander, Director

Galerie argus-fotokunst
Marienstrasse 26
Berlin, D-10117, Germany
tel: 49-30-283-59-01
fax: 49-30-283-30-49
e-mail: mail@gallery-argus.com
web: www.gallery-argus.com
Norbert Bunge, Director

Deborah Bell Photographs
511 West 25th Street, Room 703
New York, NY 10001
tel: 212-691-3883
fax: 212-691-3222
e-mail: deborahbell@rcn.com
web: www.deborahbellphotographs.com
Deborah Bell
Adam Bezer

Joseph Bellows Gallery
7661 Girard Avenue
La Jolla, CA 92037
tel: 858-456-5620
fax: 858-456-5621
e-mail: info@josephbellows.com
web: www.josephbellows.com
Joseph Bellows
Carol Lee Brosseau
Nicole Moffatt

Bonni Benrubi Gallery, Inc.
41 East 57th Street
New York, NY 10022
tel: 212-888-6007
fax: 212-751-0819
e-mail: benrubi@bonnibenrubi.com
web: www.bonnibenrubi.com
Bonni Benrubi
Thom Vogel
Katie Crook
Luis Peralta

Sandra Berler Gallery
7002 Connecticut Avenue
Chevy Chase, MD 20815
tel: 301-656-8144
fax: 301-656-8182
e-mail: sandra.berler@verizon.net
web: www.sandraberlergallery.com
Sandra Berler, Director

Galerie Daniel Blau
Odeonsplatz 12
Munich, 80539, Germany
tel: 49-89-29-73-42
fax: 49-89-24-20-48-60
e-mail: contact@danielblau.de
web: www.danielblau.de
Daniel Blau
Nicole Gnesa

Janet Borden, Inc.
560 Broadway #601
New York, NY 10012
tel: 212-431-0166
fax: 212-279-1679
e-mail: info@janetbordeninc.com
web: www.janetbordeninc.com
Janet Borden
Matthew Whitworth
Brandon Schneider
Susan Stevenson
Betsy Stapleton

J.J. Brookings Gallery
330 Commercial Street
San Jose, CA 95112
tel: 408-287-3311
fax: 408-287-6075
e-mail: info@jjbrookings.com
web: www.jjbrookings.com
Timothy C. Duran, Gallery Director
Teresa Hanson, Gallery Manager

Stephen Bulger Gallery
1026 Queen Street West
Toronto, Ontario, M6J 1H6 Canada
tel: 416-504-0575
fax: 416-504-8929
e-mail: info@bulgergallery.com
web: www.bulgergallery.com
Stephen Bulger
Sanaz Mazinani
Anthony Koutras
David Stevenson
Natalie Spagnol

**Robert Burge/20th Century
Photographs, Ltd.**
315 East 62nd Street
New York, NY 10021
tel: 212-838-4108
fax: 212-838-4390
e-mail: antiques@yaleburge.com
web: www.yaleburge.com
Robert Burge
Ruth Butler
Jerry Jones

Byron McMahon Gallery
New Address
88 George Street
Redfern Sydney, NSW 2016, Australia
tel: 61-2-9318-0404
fax: 61-2-9318-0004
e-mail: info@byronmcmahongallery.com.au
web: www.byronmcmahongallery.com.au
Sandra Byron, Director
Peter McMahon, Director
Erin O'Moore, Gallery Manager

Camera Obscura Gallery
1309 Bannock Street
Denver, CO 80204
tel/fax: 303-623-4059
e-mail: info@cameraobscuragallery.com
web: www.cameraobscuragallery.com
Hal Gould, Director
Loretta Young-Gautier, Associate Director

galerie michèle chomette
24 rue Beaubourg
Paris, 75003, France
tel: 33-1-42-78-05-62
fax: 33-1-42-72-62-05
e-mail: mc.galerie@free.fr
Michèle Chomette, Owner/Director

Galerie Clairefontaine
7, Place de Clairefontaine
1341, Luxembourg
and 21, rue du Saint-Esprit
1475, Luxembourg
tel: 352-47-23-24
fax: 352-47-25-24
e-mail: galerie.clairefontaine@pt.lu
web: www.galerie-clairefontaine.lu
Dr. Marita Ruiter, Owner/Director

Stephen L. Clark Gallery
1101 West Sixth Street
Austin, TX 78703
tel: 512-477-0828
fax: 512-477-0934
e-mail: slcgallery@mac.com
web: www.artnet.com/slclark.html
Stephen Clark, Owner
Amber Levis, Gallery Director

John Cleary Gallery
2635 Colquitt
Houston, TX 77098
tel: 713-524-5070
e-mail: info@johnclearygallery.com
web: www.johnclearygallery.com
John Cleary
Catherine Couturier

Stephen Cohen Gallery, Inc.
7358 Beverly Boulevard
Los Angeles, CA 90036
tel: 323-937-5525
fax: 323-937-5523
e-mail: info@stephencohengallery.com
web: www.stephencohengallery.com
Stephen Cohen, Owner
Beverly Feldman, Gallery Director
Rick Perez, Assistant Director
Jean-Paul Biondi- Gallery Manager
Danny Jauregui, Gallery Assistant

Commerce Graphics Ltd, Inc.
506 East 74th Street
New York, NY 10021
tel: 212-517-7648
fax: 212-517-7649
e-mail: info@commercegraphics.com
Ron Kurtz, President
Cindy Johnson, Director
Natalie Evans, Associate Director

Contemporary Works / Vintage Works, LTD.
258 Inverness Circle
Chalfont, PA 18914
tel: 215-822-5662
fax: 215-822-8003
e-mail: info@vintageworks.net
web: www.vintageworks.net
www.iphotocentral.com
www.contemporaryworks.net
Alex Novak
Marthe Smith

Corkin Gallery
Distillery District
55 Mill Street, Bldg. 61
Toronto Ontario, M5A 3C4, Canada
tel: 416-979-1980
fax: 416-979-7018
e-mail: info@corkingallery.com
web: www.corkingallery.com
Jane Corkin

Charles Cowles Gallery
537 West 24th Street
New York, NY 10011
tel: 212-741-8999
fax: 212-741-6222
e-mail: info@cowlesgallery.com
web: www.cowlesgallery.com
Charles Cowles

Czech Center of Photography
Hybernska 7a
Prague 1, 110 00, Czech Republic
tel/fax: 420-296-522-284
e-mail: ccf@volny.cz
web: www.greisen.cz
Jiri Jaskmanicky, Director

Stephen Daiter Gallery / Daiter Contemporary
311 West Superior Street, # 404 & 408
Chicago, IL 60610
tel: 312-787-3350
fax: 312-787-3354
e-mail: info@stephendaitergallery.com
web: www.stephendaitergallery.com
Stephen Daiter
Paul Berlanga
Michael Welch

David Gallery
5797 Washington Boulevard
Culver City, CA 90232
tel: 323-939-9069
fax: 323-939-9079
e-mail: info@davidgallery.net
web: www.davidgallery.net
David Barenholtz
Joshua Holzmann

Michael Dawson Gallery
535 North Larchmont Boulevard
Los Angeles, CA 90004
tel: 323-469-2186
fax: 323-469-9553
e-mail: info@michaeldawsongallery.com
web: www.michaeldawsongallery.com
Michael Dawson

Keith de Lellis Gallery
Mailing address until June 2007
141 E 88th Street, Apt 4A
New York, NY 10128
tel: 212-410-5440
tel: 917-533-4964
New address June 2007
1045 Madison Avenue
New York, NY 10075
tel: 212-327-1482
fax: 212-327-1492
e-mail: keith@keithdelellisgallery.com
web: www.keithdelellisgallery.com
Keith de Lellis, Director

Candace Dwan Gallery
24 West 57th Street, Suite 503
New York, NY 10019
tel: 212-315-0065
fax: 212-315-2220
27 Katonah Avenue
Katonah, NY 10536
tel/fax: 914-232-3966
e-mail: email@candacedwan.com
web: www.candacedwan.com
Candace Dwan, Director
Christine Stamas, Gallery Manager, NY
Alexa Coyne, Gallery Manager, Katonah

Catherine Edelman Gallery
300 West Superior Street, Lower Level
Chicago, IL 60610
tel: 312-266-2350
fax: 312-266-1967
e-mail: catherine@edelmangallery.com
web: www.edelmangallery.com
Catherine Edelman, Director
Melanie Pankau, Assistant Director
Marissa Baker, Preparator

Gary Edwards Gallery
1711 Connecticut Avenue, NW
Washington, DC 20009
tel: 301-524-0900
e-mail: garymedwards@mac.com
Gary Edwards, Director

Etherton Gallery
135 South 6th Avenue
Tucson, AZ 85701
tel: 520-624-7370
fax: 520-792-4569
e-mail: info@ethertongallery.com
web: www.ethertongallery.com
Terry Etherton, President
Hannah Glasston, Gallery Director
Daphne Srinivasan, Publicist
Dawne Osborne, Registrar

Kathleen Ewing Gallery
New address
1767 P Street, NW Suite 3
Washington, DC 20036
tel: 202-328-0955
fax: 202-462-1019
e-mail: ewingal@aol.com
web: www.kathleenewinggallery.com
Kathleen Ewing, Owner/Director
Charlotte Vazquez, Assistant Director
JoAnne Ewing, Assistant to the Director
Ingrid Yan, Gallery Assistant

Galerie Johannes Faber
Brahmsplatz 7
Vienna, 1040, Austria
tel/fax: 43-1-505-75-18
e-mail: office@jmcfaber.at
web: www.jmcfaber.at
Johannes Faber
Michaela Hüttner

Fahey/Klein Gallery

148 North La Brea Avenue
Los Angeles, CA 90036
tel: 323-934-2250
fax: 323-934-4243
e-mail: fkg@earthlink.net
web: www.faheykleingallery.com
David Fahey, Co-owner
Ken Devlin, Co-owner
James Gilbert, Associate Director
Gisele Schmidt, Associate Director
Stephen Heer, Registrar

Henry Feldstein

PO Box 398
Forest Hills, NY 11375
tel: 718-544-3002
fax: 718-544-7139
e-mail: henryfe@ix.netcom.com
Henry Feldstein, Director

Peter Fetterman Gallery

2525 Michigan Avenue, #A7
Santa Monica, CA 90404
tel: 310-453-6463
fax: 310-453-6959
e-mail: info@peterfetterman.com
web: www.peterfetterman.com
Peter Fetterman, Owner & Director
Sam Lee, Director
Marco Paez, Assistant Director

Wm. Floyd

PO Box 1628 Lenox Hill Station
New York, NY 10021
tel: 212-365-0658
e-mail: wmfloyd@verizon.net
web: www.floydgallery.com
William L. Floyd
Lyle Cavanaugh

Fraenkel Gallery

49 Geary Street
San Francisco, CA 94108
tel: 415-981-2661
fax: 415-981-4014
e-mail: mail@fraenkelgallery.com
web: www.fraenkelgallery.com
Jeffrey Fraenkel, President
Frish Brandt, Director
Elizabeth Chiles, Associate Director

Eric Franck Fine Art

61 Willow Walk, 1st floor, Unit 8010,
London, SE1 5SF, England
tel: 44-207-394-9743
fax: 44-207-394-1956
e-mail: e.franck@btclick.com
Eric Franck
Elizabeth Smith
Judith Platte

Barry Friedman Ltd.

32 East 67th Street
New York, NY 10021
tel: 212-794-8950
fax: 212-794-8889
e-mail: contact@barryfriedmanltd.com
web: www.barryfriedmanltd.com
Barry Friedman
Marc Benda
Carole Hochman
Lisa Jensen
Spencer Tsai
Erika Brandt

Gallery 19/21

9 Little Harbor Road
Guilford, CT 06437
tel: 203-453-6215
fax: 203-453-5612
e-mail: gallery19th21st@aol.com
web: gallery19th21st.free.fr
Florence Pénault

Galerie 1900/2000

8 rue Bonaparte
Paris, 75006, France
tel: 33-1-43-25-84-20
fax: 33-1-46-34-74-52
e-mail: dfleiss@galerie1900-2000.com
web: www.galerie1900-2000.com
David Fleiss
Marcel Fleiss
Eleonore Malingue, Contact in New York

G. Gibson Gallery
300 South Washington Street
Seattle, WA 98104
tel: 206-587-4033
fax: 206-587-5751
e-mail: gail@ggibsongallery.com
web: www.ggibsongallery.com
Gail Gibson
Claudia Vernia
K.C. Potter de Haan

Gitterman Gallery
170 East 75th Street
New York, NY 10021
tel: 212-734-0868
fax: 212-734-0869
e-mail: info@gittermangallery.com
web: www.gittermangallery.com
Tom Gitterman
Abigail Feldman
Elena John

Fay Gold Gallery
764 Miami Circle
Atlanta, GA 30324
tel: 404-233-3843
fax: 404-365-8633
e-mail: info@faygoldgallery.com
web: www.faygoldgallery.com
Fay Gold
Amy Miller
Veronica Kessenich

Howard Greenberg Gallery
41 East 57th Street, Suite 1406
New York, NY 10022
tel: 212-334-0010
fax: 212-941-7479
e-mail: info@howardgreenberg.com
web: www.howardgreenberg.com
Howard Greenberg
Margit Erb
Karen Marks

HackelBury Fine Art Limited
4 Launceston Place
London, W8 5RL, England
tel: 44-207-937-8688
fax: 44-207-937-8868
e-mail: gallery@hackelbury.co.uk
web: www.hackelbury.co.uk
Marcus Bury
Sascha Hackel
Kate Stevens

The Halsted Gallery
PO Box 130
Bloomfield Hills, MI 48303
tel: 248-745-0062
e-mail: info@halstedgallery.com
web: www.halstedgallery.com
Thomas Halsted
Wendy Halsted Beard

Charles A. Hartman Fine Art
2625 NE 26th Avenue
Portland, OR 97212
tel: 503-287-3886
e-mail: charles@hartmanfineart.net
web: www.hartmanfineart.net
Charles A. Hartman

HASTED HUNT
529 West 20th Street, 3rd floor
New York, NY 10011
tel: 212-627-0006
fax: 212-627-5117
e-mail: info@hastedhunt.com
web: www.hastedhunt.com
Sarah Hasted
W.M. Hunt
Mary-Presely Adams, Director
Zoe Madle, Associate
Lauren Luckett, Registrar

HEMPHILL

1515 14th Street, NW
Washington, DC 20005
tel: 202-234-5601
fax: 202-234-5607
e-mail: gallery@hemphillfinearts.com
web: www.hemphillfinearts.com
George Hemphill
Mary Early
Kimberly Graham
Jessica Lawrence

Laurent Herschtritt

182 Chemin du Cros
Six Fours Les Plages, 83140, France
tel: 33-6-07-85-63-00
fax: 33-4-94-07-38-76
e-mail: rememberphoto@free.fr
web: www.remember.fr
Laurent Herschtritt

Robert Hershkowitz Ltd.

Cockhaise, Monteswood Lane
Near Lindfield
Sussex, RH16 2QP, England
tel: 44-1444-482-240
fax: 44-1444-484-777
e-mail: prhfoto@hotmail.com
3 Sloane Avenue
London, SW3 3JD, England
tel: 44-20-7581-0362
Robert Hershkowitz, Director
Paula Hershkowitz, Director

Paul M. Hertzmann, Inc.

PO Box 40447
San Francisco, CA 94140
tel: 415-626-2677
fax: 415-552-4160
e-mail: pmhi@hertzmann.net
Paul Hertzmann, Director
Susan Herzig, Director

Michael Hoppen Gallery Ltd.

3 Jubilee Place
London, SW3 3TD, England
tel: 207-352-3649
fax: 207-352-3669
e-mail:
gallery@michaelhoppengallery.com
web: www.michaelhoppengallery.com
Michael Hoppen
Kathlene Caldwell
Lucy Chadwick

Edwynn Houk Gallery

745 Fifth Avenue
New York, NY 10151
tel: 212-750-7070
fax: 212-688-4848
e-mail: info@houkgallery.com
web: www.houkgallery.com
Edwynn Houk
Julie Castellano
Kirsten Bengtson
John Cowey
Jack Early
Payal Parekh
Erik Rocca

Hyperion Press Limited

200 West 86th Street
New York, NY 10024
tel: 212-877-2131
fax: 212-769-3907
e-mail: hyperionpr@verizon.net
Monah L. Gettner, Director
Alan Gettner, Co-Director
Dawn Luebbe, Assistant Director

Charles Isaacs Photographs, Inc.

25 West 54th Street, # 5C
New York, NY 10019
tel: 212-957-3238
e-mail: cti@charlesisaacs.com
web: www.charlesisaacs.com
Charles Isaacs
Carol Nigro

Jackson Fine Art
3115 East Shadowlawn Avenue
Atlanta, GA 30305
tel: 404-233-3739
fax: 404-233-1205
e-mail: malia@jacksonfineart.com
web: www.jacksonfineart.com
Anna Walker Skillman, Owner
Malia Stewart, Director
Morgan Beasley
Stephanie Dowda, Administrator
Stevie Brown

Ken & Jenny Jacobson
Southcotts Petches Bridge
Great Bardfield, Essex
CM7 4QN, England
tel: 441-371-810-566
fax: 441-371-810-845
e-mail: ken@jacobsonphoto.com
web: www.jacobsonphoto.com
Ken Jacobson, Director
Jenny Jacobson, Director

Steven Kasher Gallery
521 West 23rd Street, 2nd Floor
New York, NY 10011
tel: 212-966-3978
fax: 212-226-1485
e-mail: info@stevenkasher.com
web: www.stevenkasher.com
Steven Kasher
Gary Owen
Maria Stenina

Jan Kesner Gallery
164 North La Brea Avenue
Los Angeles, CA 90036-2912
tel: 323-938-6834
fax: 323-938-1106
e-mail:
jankesner@jankesnergallery.com
web: www.jankesnergallery.com
Jan Kesner
Justen Deal

Kicken Berlin
Linienstrasse 155 / 161a
Berlin, 10115, Germany
tel: 49-30-288-77-88-2
fax: 49-30-288-77-88-3
e-mail: kicken@kicken-gallery.com
web: www.kicken-gallery.com
Annette Kicken
Rudolf Kicken

Robert Klein Gallery
38 Newbury Street, 4th Floor
Boston, MA 02116
tel: 617-267-7997
fax: 617-267-5567
e-mail: inquiry@robertkleingallery.com
web: www.robertkleingallery.com
Robert Klein
Eunice Hurd
Drea Plummer
Jessica Turner

Alan Klotz Gallery
511 West 25th Street Suite 701
New York, NY 10001
tel: 212-741-4764
fax: 212-741-4760
e-mail: info@klotzgallery.com
web: www.klotzgallery.com
Alan Klotz, Director
Peter C. Emerick, Gallery Manager

Robert Koch Gallery
49 Geary Street, 5th Floor
San Francisco, CA 94108
tel: 415-421-0122
fax: 415-421-6306
e-mail: info@kochgallery.com
web: www.kochgallery.com
Robert Koch
Ada Takahashi

Paul Kopeikin Gallery
6150 Wilshire Boulevard
Los Angeles, CA 90048
tel: 323-937-0765
fax: 323-937-5974
e-mail: info@paulkopeikingallery.com
web: www.paulkopeikingallery.com
Paul Kopeikin
Kaycee Olsen

Hans P. Kraus, Jr., Inc.
962 Park Avenue at 82nd Street
New York, NY 10028
tel: 212-794-2064
fax: 212-744-2770
e-mail: info@sunpictures.com
Hans P. Kraus, Jr.
Jennifer Parkinson
Russell Lord
Shelley Dowell

Patricia Laligant Gallery
150 West 28th Street, Suite 1702
New York, NY 10001
tel: 212-252-9922
e-mail: patricialaligant@msn.com
web: www.patricialaligant.com
Patricia Laligant

baudoin lebon
38, rue Sainte Croix de la Bretonnerie
Paris, 75004, France
tel: 33-1-42-72-09-10
fax: 33-1-42-72-02-20
e-mail: baudoin.lebon@wanadoo.fr
web: www.baudoin-lebon.com
Baudoin Lebon
Anne Le Tri
Caroline Bouchard

Josef Lebovic Gallery
PO Box 453
34 Paddington Street
Paddington, NSW 2021
Sydney, Australia
tel: 61-2-9332-1840
fax: 61-2-9331-7431
e-mail: josef@joseflebovicgallery.com
web: www.joseflebovicgallery.com
Josef Lebovic, Owner
Jeanne M. Lebovic, Owner

Lee Gallery
Nine Mount Vernon Street, 2nd Floor
Winchester, MA 01890
tel: 781-729-7445
fax: 781-729-4592
e-mail: apd@leegallery.com
web: www.leegallery.com
Mack Lee, Director
Michael Lee
Erica Lee

Janet Lehr, Inc.
891 Park Avenue
New York, NY 10021
tel: 212-288-1802
fax: 212-288-6234
e-mail: janetlehr@janetlehrinc.com
web: www.janetlehrinc.com
Weekends and Summers
Vered Gallery, 68 Park Place
East Hampton, NY 11937
tel: 631-324-3303
Janet Lehr
Nicolas Hoyos
Damien Roman
Vered

Lewis Lehr, Inc.
444 East 86th Street
New York, NY 10028
tel: 212-288-6765
fax: 212-288-5067
e-mail: daguerre39@aol.com
Lewis Lehr

gallery luisotti
2525 Michigan Avenue, # A-2
Santa Monica, CA 90404
tel: 310-453-0043
fax: 310-264-4888
e-mail: info@galleryluisotti.com
web: www.artnet.com/luisotti.html
Theresa Luisotti, Owner

Ezra Mack
Mailing Address:
PO Box 5090
Greenwich, CT 06831
tel: 310-863-3467
e-mail: fineartcom@aol.com
Ezra Mack, Director

Robert Mann Gallery
210 Eleventh Avenue, 10th Floor
New York, NY 10001
tel: 212-989-7600
fax: 212-989-2947
e-mail: mail@robertmann.com
web: www.robertmann.com
Robert Mann
Caroline Cohen
Devin Grosz

Lee Marks Fine Art
2208 East 350 North
Shelbyville, IN 46176
tel: 317-398-9212
fax: 317-398-2242
e-mail: lee@leemarksfineart.com
web: www.leemarksfineart.com
Lee Marks
John C. DePrez, Jr.

McNamara Gallery Photography
190 Wicksteed Street
Wanganui 4500, New Zealand
tel: 64-6-348-7320
e-mail: mcnamaraphotogal@xtra.co.nz
web: www.mcnamara.co.nz
Paul McNamara

Ariel Meyerowitz
4720 Center Blvd., Suite 2005
Long Island City, NY 11109
tel: 212-414-2770
fax: 212-961-0505
e-mail: ariel@arielmeyerowitz.com
web: www.arielmeyerowitz.com
Ariel Meyerowitz

Laurence Miller Gallery
20 West 57th Street
New York, NY 10019
tel: 212-397-3930
fax: 212-397-3932
e-mail: contact@laurencemillergallery.com
web: www.laurencemillergallery.com
Laurence Miller, President
Vicki Harris, Director
Mark Mann, Associate Director
Jody Berman, Assistant Director

Robert Miller Gallery
524 West 26th Street
New York, NY 10001
tel: 212-366-4774
fax: 212-366-4454
e-mail: rmg@robertmillergallery.com
web: www.robertmillergallery.com
Betsy Wittenborn Miller
Robert Peter Miller
Royce Howes

Yossi Milo Gallery
525 West 25th Street
New York, NY 10001
tel: 212-414-0370
fax: 212-414-0371
e-mail: mail@yossimilo.com
web: www.yossimilo.com
Yossi Milo, Owner
Alissa Schoenfeld, Director

Richard Moore Photographs
PO Box 16245
Oakland, CA 94610
tel: 510-271-0149
fax: 510-645-1194
e-mail: rdmphoto@earthlink.net
web: www.richardmoorephoto.com
Richard D. Moore

Scott Nichols Gallery

49 Geary Street, Suite 415
San Francisco, CA 94108
tel: 415-788-4641
fax: 415-788-8438
e-mail: sngphoto@pacbell.net
web: www.scottnicholsgallery.com
Scott Nichols

Pace/MacGill Gallery

32 East 57th Street, 9th Floor
New York, NY 10022
tel: 212-759-7999
fax: 212-759-8964
e-mail: info@pacemacgill.com
web: www.pacemacgill.com
Peter MacGill
Kimberly Jones
Lauren Panzo
Irene Papanestor
Amanda Bowker

Galerie Priska Pasquer

Goebenstrasse 3
Cologne, 50672, Germany
tel: 49-221-952-6313
fax: 49-221-952 6373
e-mail: galerie@priskapasquer.de
web: www.priskapasquer.de
Priska Pasquer
Ferdinand Brueggemann

Galerie Françoise Paviot

57 rue Sainte-Anne
Paris, 75002, France
tel: 33-1-42-60-10-01
fax: 33-1-42-60-44-77
e-mail: info@paviotfoto.com
web: www.paviotfoto.com
Françoise Paviot
Alain Paviot

PhotoArt

Rathausstrasse 13 / V
Hamburg, 20095, Germany
tel: 49-40-460-1782
fax: 49-40-460-1783
e-mail: erma@photo-art-hamburg.de
web: www.photo-art-hamburg.de
Erma Schmidt-Staerz, Director

Photo Gallery International

4-12-32 Shibaura, Minato-ku
Tokyo, 108-0023, Japan
tel: 81-3-3455-7827
fax: 81-3-3455-8143
e-mail: info-e@pgi.ac
web: www.pgi.ac
Shin Yamazaki, Director
Akiko Yamada, Assistant Director

The Photographers' Gallery

5 & 8 Great Newport Street
London, WC2H 7HY, England
tel: 44-207-831-1772
fax: 44-207-836-9704
e-mail: printsales@photonet.org.uk
web: www.photonet.org.uk
Zoe Bingham
Katrina Moore
David Low

Photographs Do Not Bend Gallery

1202 Dragon Street, Suite 103
Dallas, TX 75207
tel: 214-969-1852
fax: 214-745-9901
e-mail: info@pdnbgallery.com
web: www.pdnbgallery.com
Burt Finger, Gallery Director
Missy Smith Finger, Director
Jennifer Fluegge, Assistant Director

Photology

Via Della Moscova, 25
Milan, 20121, Italy
tel: 39-02-659-5285
fax: 39-02-65-4284
e-mail: photology@photology.com
web: www.photology.com
Davide Faccioli, Director

Picture Photo Space, Inc.
Shouto Building, 2F
1-8-9 Nishi-sinsaibashi
Chuo-ku, Osaka 542-0086, Japan
tel: 81-6-6251-3225
fax: 81-6-6251-3245
e-mail: yhy12636@nifty.com
web: www.picturephotospace.com
Masato Aino, Director

Serge Plantureux
4 Galerie Vivienne
Paris, 75002, France
tel: 33-1-53-29-92-00
fax: 33-1-47-03-08-85
e-mail: info@sergeplantureux.fr
web: www.sergeplantureux.fr
Serge Plantureux
Anne-Rose de Fontainieu
Jean-Mathieu Martini
Matthias Olmeta
Adnan Sezer

Prakapas Gallery
1 Northgate, 6B
Bronxville, NY 10708
tel: 914-961-5091
fax: 914-961-5192
e-mail: eugeneprakapas@earthlink.net
Eugene J. Prakapas, Director
Dorothy Prakapas, Director

The Ralls Collection, Inc.
1516 31st Street, NW
Washington, DC 20007
tel: 202-342-1754
fax: 202-342-0141
e-mail: maralls@aol.com
web: www.rallscollection.com
Marsha Ralls, Director
Lindsay Williams, Assistant

Yancey Richardson Gallery
535 West 22nd Street
New York, NY 10011
tel: 646-230-9610
fax: 646-230-6131
e-mail: info@yanceyrichardson.com
web: www.yanceyrichardson.com
Yancey Richardson
David Carmona
Tracey Norman

RoseGallery
2525 Michigan Avenue, G-5
Santa Monica, CA 90404
tel: 310-264-8440
fax: 310-264-8443
e-mail: info@rosegallery.net
web: www.rosegallery.net
Rose Shoshana
Laura Peterson
Hannah Sloan
Andy Stolarek
Molly Toberer
Nicole Katz

Richard T. Rosenthal
4718 Springfield Avenue
Philadelphia, PA 19143
tel: 215-726-5493
fax: 215-726-5926
e-mail: rtrphoto@vernacularphotography.com
web: www.vernacularphotography.com
Richard T. Rosenthal
Janet Shilling

Julie Saul Gallery
535 West 22nd Street, 6th Floor
New York, NY 10011
tel: 212-627-2410
fax: 212-627-2411
e-mail: mail@saulgallery.com
web: www.saulgallery.com
Julie Saul
Edna Cardinali
Lisa Fontana

William L. Schaeffer/Photographs
PO Box 296
Chester, CT 06412
tel: 860-526-3870
William L. Schaeffer, Director
Arthur Weisenburger, Assistant Director

Scheinbaum & Russek Ltd.
369 Montezuma, #345
Santa Fe, NM 87501
tel: 505-988-5116
fax: 505-988-4346
e-mail: srltd@photographydealers.com
web: www.photographydealers.com
Janet Russek, Director
David Scheinbaum, Director
Sharon Russell, Administrative Assistant

Howard Schickler Fine Art
PO Box 49227
Sarasota, FL 34230
tel: 941-366-2128
e-mail: gallery@schicklerart.com
web: www.schicklerart.com
Howard Schickler

Charles Schwartz Ltd.
21 East 90th Street
New York, NY 10128
tel: 212-534-4496
fax: 212-534-0313
e-mail: cms@cs-photo.com
web: www.cs-photo.com
Charles Schwartz
Annick Rosenfield

Michael Senft / Masterworks
PO Box 3117
East Hampton, NY 11937
tel: 631-907-0904
fax: 631-907-9795
e-mail: michaelsenft@optonline.net
Michael Senft

Lisa Sette Gallery
4142 North Marshall Way
Scottsdale, AZ 85251
tel: 480-990-7342
fax: 480-970-0825
e-mail: sette@lisasettegallery.com
web: www.lisasettegallery.com
Lisa Sette, Director
Duane D. Smith, Associate Director
Ashley Rice, Director of Photography
Michael Mulno, Special Projects
Helen E. Raleigh, Web Mistress
Elena Lourenco, Preparator

Michael Shapiro Photographs
49 Geary Street, Suite 208
San Francisco, CA 94108
tel: 415-398-6655
fax: 415-398-0667
e-mail: info@shapirogallery.net
web: www.shapirogallery.net
Michael Shapiro
Enrico Cittadino

Silverstein Photography
535 West 24th Street
New York, NY 10011
tel: 212-627-3930
fax: 212-691-5509
e-mail:
inquiries@silversteinphotography.com
web: www.silversteinphotography.com
Bruce Silverstein
Elizabeth Shank
Liam Derik van Loenen
Luis Escalera
Yvonne Gomez

Barry Singer Gallery
7 Western Avenue
Petaluma, CA 94952
tel: 707-781-3200
fax: 707-781-3030
e-mail: singer@singergallery.com
web: www.singergallery.com
Barry Singer
Gretchen Singer

Andrew Smith Gallery, Inc.
203 West San Francisco Street
Santa Fe, NM 87501
tel: 505-984-1234
fax: 505-983-2428
e-mail: info@andrewsmithgallery.com
web: www.andrewsmithgallery.com
Andrew Smith, President
John Boland, Associate Director
Christopher Marquez

Joel Soroka Gallery
400 East Hyman Avenue
Aspen, CO 81611
tel: 970-920-3152
fax: 970-920-3823
e-mail: joelsoroka@msn.com
Joel Soroka

Staley-Wise Gallery
560 Broadway, Suite 305
New York, NY 10012
tel: 212-966-6223
fax: 212-966-6293
e-mail: photo@staleywise.com
web: www.staleywise.com
Etheleen Staley, Director
Takouhy Wise, Director

John Stevenson Gallery
338 West 23rd Street
New York, NY 10011-2201
tel: 212-352-0070
fax: 212-741-6449
e-mail:
mail@johnstevenson-gallery.com
web: www.johnstevenson-gallery.com
John Stevenson, Director
Will Story, Manager & Curator

Galerie Zur Stockeregg
Stockerstrasse 33
Zürich, 8022, Switzerland
tel: 41-44-202-69-25
fax: 41-44-202-82-51
e-mail: info@stockeregg.com
web: www.stockeregg.com
Kaspar M. Fleischmann, Director
Claudia Coellen Helbling,
Assistant Director
Beatrice Amstutz, Administration

TARTT/washington
1711 Connecticut Avenue, NW
Washington, DC 20009
tel: 202-256-7343
e-mail: jctjr@earthlink.net
Jo C. Tartt, Jr.

Throckmorton Fine Art, Inc.
145 East 57th Street, 3rd floor
New York, NY 10022
tel: 212-223-1059
fax: 212-223-1937
e-mail: info@throckmorton-nyc.com
web: www.throckmorton-nyc.com
Spencer Throckmorton, Owner
Kraige Block, Director
Luke Leonard, Photo Registrar /
Graphic Designer
Jessica Curnoe, Antiquities Registrar
Sean Cleary, Art Handler

Vision Gallery
PO Box 2101
18 Yosef Rivlin Street
Jerusalem, 91020, Israel
tel: 972-2-622-2253
fax: 972-2-622-2269
e-mail: vision@visiongallery.com
web: www.visiongallery.com
Neil Folberg
Anna Folberg
Yehuda Folberg

Wach Gallery

31860 Walker Road
Avon Lake, OH 44012
tel: 440-933-2780
fax: 440-933-2781
e-mail: mail@wachgallery.com
web: www.wachgallery.com
Peter M. Wach
Judith Wach

Weinstein Gallery

908 West 46th Street
Minneapolis, MN 55419
tel: 612-822-1722
fax: 612-822-1745
e-mail: weingall@aol.com
web: www.weinstein-gallery.com
Martin Weinstein
Laura Hoyt, Director

Wessel + O'Connor Fine Art

111 Front Street, Suite 200
Dumbo, Brooklyn, NY 11201
tel: 718-596-1700
fax: 718-596-1764
e-mail: wesseloconnor@aol.com
web: www.wesseloconnor.com
William C. O'Connor
John C. Wessel

The Weston Gallery, Inc.

6th Avenue / Dolores & Lincoln
PO Box 655
Carmel, CA 93921
tel: 831-624-4453
fax: 831-624-7190
e-mail: info@westongallery.com
web: www.westongallery.com
Maggi Weston, President
Richard Gadd, Director

Winter Works on Paper

160 Fifth Avenue, #718
New York, NY 10010
tel: 212-352-9013
fax: 718-388-5217
e-mail: winterworks@verizon.net
web: www.winterworksonpaper.com
David Winter

Galerie Esther Woerdehoff

36, rue Falguière
Paris, 75015, France
tel: 33-1-43-21-44-83
fax: 33-1-43-21-45-03
e-mail: galerie@ewgalerie.com
web: www.ewgalerie.com
Esther Woerdehoff
Beatrice Rossetto
Sara Bertilsson

Zabriskie Gallery

41 East 57th Street, 4th Floor
New York, NY 10022
tel: 212-752-1223
fax: 212-752-1224
e-mail: info@zabriskiegallery.com
web: www.zabriskiegallery.com
Virginia Zabriskie, Owner
Alexis Dean, Associate Director
Jonathan Spies, Associate Director

Illustrated Catalogue Entries

Alphabetical Listing

© Clarence John Laughlin, *The Enigma,* 1941

A Gallery For Fine Photography

241 Chartres Street
New Orleans, LA 70130

tel: 504-568-1313
fax: 504-568-1322
e-mail: joshuamann@att.net
web: www.agallery.com

Joshua Mann Pailet, Chief
Edward Hébert, Director

Hours: Thursday - Monday 10-6

Founded 1973
Rare Photographs and Books

Featuring

Henri Cartier-Bresson
Ansel Adams
Helmut Newton
Herman Leonard
Jerry Uelsmann
Elliott Erwitt
Josephine Sacabo
Sandy Skoglund
Jan Saudek
Edward Sheriff Curtis
André Kertész
W. Eugene Smith
Peter Beard

Bruce Barnbaum
Birney Imes
Edward Steichen
Alfred Stieglitz
Fonville Winans
Yousuf Karsh
Laure Albin-Guillot
Joshua Mann Pailet
Walker Evans
Brett Weston
Edward Weston
Marion Post-Wolcott
Clarence John Laughlin

Alexey Titarenko, *Untitled (Heads),* 1992
City of Shadows series

Nailya Alexander

24 West 57th Street, #503
New York, NY 10019

tel: 212-315-2211
fax: 212-315-2220
e-mail: nailya@mindspring.com
web: www.nailyaalexandergallery.com

Nailya Alexander, Director

Hours: Tuesday - Saturday 11-6

Soviet (1930-1960) and Contemporary Photography

Representing
Andrey Chezhin
Lori Grinker
Evgeny Mokhorev
Igor Savchenko
Alexey Titarenko
Remigijus Treigys
Max Penson Estate

Works available by
Max Alpert
Lev Borodulin
Colby Caldwell
Mikhail Grachev
Alexander Grinberg
Boris Ignatovich
Evgeny Khaldey
Yakov Khalip
Nikolai Kubeev
Georgy Lipskerov
Georgy Petrusov
Lucian Perkins

Aleksandr Rodchenko
Vladimir Kuprianov
Moisei Nappelbaum
Arkady Shaikhet
Ivan Shagin
Sergey Shimansky
Boris Smelov
Antanas Sutkus
Vasiliy Ulitin
Beatrice Valdes Paz
Georgy Zelma
Alexander Zhitomirsky

Max Penson, *Youth of Bukhara Arrived in Tashkent*, 1936

Karl Ewald, *Berlin, 1928*
Vintage silver prints

Galerie argus-fotokunst

Marienstrasse 26
Berlin, 10117, Germany

tel: 49-30-283-59-01
fax: 49-30-283-30-49
e-mail: mail@gallery-argus.com
web: www.gallery-argus.com

Norbert Bunge, Director

Hours: Tuesday - Saturday 2-6

20th Century and Contemporary Photography

Specializing in photographs by Dr. Paul Wolff and East German Photography.

Works by	**Representing**
Ursula Arnold	Ragnar Axelsson
Ragnar Axelsson	René Burri
Sibylle Bergemann	Horacio Coppola
Christian Borchert	Karl Ewald
Krass Clement	Arno Fischer
Karl Ewald	Leonard Freed
George Friedmann	René Friede
Arno Fischer	George Friedmann
Brian Graham	Ara Güler
Konrad Hoffmeister	Karol Kállay
Clemens Kalischer	Clemens Kalischer
Robert Lebeck	Dunja Marton
Ulrich Mack	Will McBride
Ute Mahler	Manfred Paul
Manfred Paul	Antanas Sutkus
Evelyn Richter	Annette Wolff
Gundula Schulze Eldowy	Dr. Paul Wolff
Uwe Steinberg	
Ulrich Wüst	

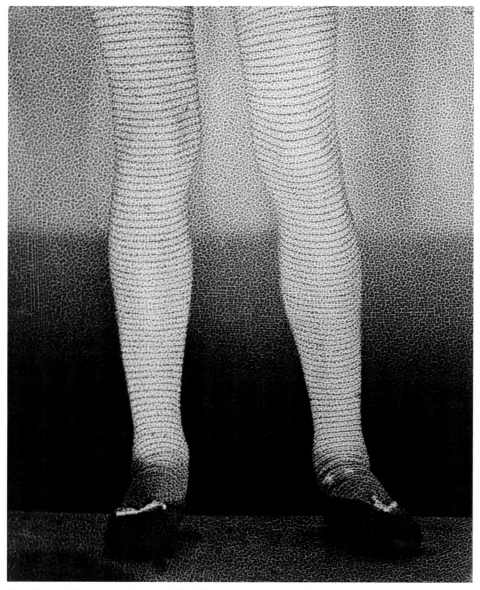

Erwin Blumenfeld (American, b. Germany, 1897-1969), *Legs à la Seurat, New York, 1942 (Maroua Motherwell)*
Gelatin silver print, made 1950s, 13 ¹/₈ x 10 ¹/₁₆ inches (33.4 x 25.6 centimeters)

Deborah Bell Photographs

511 West 25th Street, Room 703
New York, NY 10001

tel: 212-691-3883
fax: 212-691-3222
e-mail: deborahbell@rcn.com
web: www.deborahbellphotographs.com

Deborah Bell
Adam Bezer

Hours: Saturdays 12-6
And By Appointment

19th & 20th Century and Selected Contemporary Photographs

Founded in 1988. Concentrating on 20th century photography, especially American and European works from the 1920s through the 1970s, and prints by selected contemporary photographers.

Vito Acconci	Walker Evans
Josef Albers	Louis Faurer
Dag Alveng	Gerard Petrus Fieret
Eugène Atget	Edward Grazda
Per Berntsen	Peter Hujar
Erwin Blumenfeld	Sid Kaplan
Bill Brandt	Helen Levitt
The Estate of Esther Bubley	Susan Paulsen
Harry Callahan	August Sander
John Cohen	Gundula Schulze el Dowy
William Eggleston	Garry Winogrand

Robert Heinecken, *Equivocal Figure,* 1965
Vintage gelatin silver print

Joseph Bellows Gallery

7661 Girard Avenue
La Jolla, CA 92037

tel: 858-456-5620
fax: 858-456-5621
e-mail: info@josephbellows.com
web: www.josephbellows.com

Joseph Bellows
Carol Lee Brosseau
Nicole Moffatt

Hours: Tuesday - Saturday 10-6, Saturday 11-5

Fine Vintage and Contemporary Photography

Ansel Adams	Walker Evans	Han Nguyen
Kurt Baasch	Arnold Genthe	John Pfahl
John Banasiak	Emmet Gowin	J. John Priola
Virginia Beahan	Declan Haun	George Schumacher
Jayne Hinds Bidaut	Robert Heinecken	Aaron Siskind
Anne Brigman	Chip Hopper	Camille Solyagua
Wynn Bullock	Len Jenshel	Edward Sturr
Debbie Fleming Caffery	André Kertész	Dr. Dain L. Tasker
Paul Caponigro	Vilem Kriz	Alex Webb
Linda Connor	Laura Letinsky	Brett Weston
William Dassonville	Loewy & Puiseux	Edward Weston
Andre de Dienes	Leonard Misonne	Minor White
P.H. Emerson	William Mortensen	Terry Wild

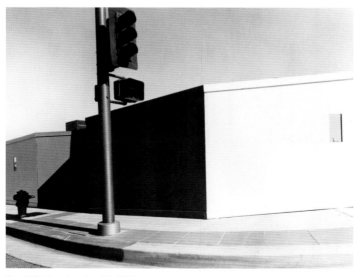

Terry Wild, *Los Angeles, CA, 1969*
Vintage gelatin silver print

Simon **Norfolk**, *King Amanullah's Victory Arch built to Celebrate the 1919 winning of independence from the British, Afghanistan,* 2003

Bonni Benrubi Gallery, Inc.

41 East 57th Street
New York, NY 10022

tel: 212-888-6007
fax: 212-751-0819
e-mail: benrubi@bonnibenrubi.com
web: www.bonnibenrubi.com

Bonni Benrubi
Thom Vogel
Katie Crook
Luis Peralta

Hours: Tuesday - Saturday 10-6

20th Century and Contemporary Photographs

Berenice Abbott
Merry Alpern
Wout Berger
Brassai
Henri Cartier-Bresson
Georges Dambier
Jed Devine
Andreas Feininger
Fernand Fonssagrives
Rena Bass Forman
Paul Fusco
Lewis Hine
Harri Kallio

Jason Langer
Jacques Henri Lartigue
Karine Laval
Gillian Laub
Jonathan Lewis
Linda McCartney
Laura McPhee
Judith McMillan
Jeffrey Milstein
Abelardo Morell
Arnold Newman
Leonard Nimoy
Simon Norfolk

Paolo Pellegrin
Matthew Pillsbury
Lindy Smith
Louis Stettner
Alfred Stieglitz
Ron van Dongen
Massimo Vitali
Hiroshi Watanabe
Christopher Woodcock
Weegee
and others

Herbert Watkins (active 1857-1873), *Alexandre Dumas*, c. 1857
Vintage albumen print on original mount (from collodion glass negative) 19.8 x 15.6 centimeters
Blind stamp on mount recto l.m.: untouched photograph, 179 Regent Street Herbert Watkins
Dedicated and signed on mount l.m.: *Madame Hugo, Alexandre Dumas*
Provenance Ex-collection Alphonsine de Saint-Amand (Album Famille Victor Hugo (B.N.F. Paris))

Galerie Daniel Blau

Odeonsplatz 12
Munich, 80539, Germany

tel: 49-89-29-73-42
fax: 49-89-24-20-48-60
e-mail: contact@danielblau.de
web: www.danielblau.de

Daniel Blau
Nicole Gnesa

Hours: Tuesday - Friday 11-6
Saturday & Monday: By Appointment

Galerie Daniel Blau, founded in 1990, specializes in modern art of the 1960's and 1970's, and 19th- and 20th-century photography. The gallery also exhibits at TEFAF in Maastricht, Art Basel and Paris Photo.

Eduard Baldus	Charles Negre	NASA
Paul Berthier	Eugene Piot	Frank Scherschel
Louis De Clercq	Georges Poulet	George Silk
Maxime Du Camp	Cecil Beaton	Eugene Smith
Jean-Baptiste Frenet	Margaret Bourke-White	William Vandivert
Charles Hugo	Jay Eyerman	Thomas Walther
Roger Fenton	Fritz Goro	Andy Warhol
Gustave Le Gray	Anselm Kiefer	
Gaudenzio Marconi	Bob Landry	

Felix Auguste Leclerc (1838-1896), *Bow of the Astrée Taken at Sea*, 1871
Vintage albumen print from the album of *Commandant Miot*, 16.8 x 21.3 centimeters

Tina Barney, *Caddies, China, 2006*
Chromogenic color print, 48 x 60 inches

Janet Borden, Inc.

560 Broadway #601
New York, NY 10012

tel: 212-431-0166
fax: 212-279-1679
e-mail: info@janetbordeninc.com
web: www.janetbordeninc.com

Janet Borden
Matthew Whitworth
Brandon Schneider
Susan Stevenson
Betsy Stapleton

Hours: Tuesday - Saturday 11-5

Contemporary Photography

Tina Barney
E.J. Bellocq
Fred Cray
Robert Cumming
Jim Dow
Macduff Everton
Lee Friedlander
Jan Groover
Andreas Magdanz
Ray Mortenson
Hanno Otten
Martin Parr
John Pfahl
Larry Sultan
Neil Winokur

Robert Burley, *Lake Superior / Thunder Bay*, 2006/2006
Chromogenic print mounted to 40 x 48 inch archival board, 30 $^1/_2$ x 39 inches

Jeff Thomas, *American Museum of Natural History*, 2001/2003
Choromogenic print, 16 x 20 inches

Stephen Bulger Gallery

1026 Queen Street West
Toronto, Ontario, M6J 1H6 Canada

tel: 416-504-0575
fax: 416-504-8929
e-mail: info@bulgergallery.com
web: www.bulgergallery.com

Stephen Bulger
Sanaz Mazinani
Anthony Koutras
David Stevenson
Natalie Spagnol

Hours: Tuesday - Saturday 11-6

Since 1995, the gallery has sustained an active exhibition schedule of both historical and contemporary photographers, from across Canada and around the world. We maintain a large inventory in a range of genres; the gallery specializes in photographs that tell stories both large and small.

Shelby Lee Adams
Dick Arentz
Jaret Belliveau
Phil Bergerson
Marco Bohr
Estate of Reva Brooks
Robert Burley
Bertrand Carrière
Estate of Douglas Clark
Scott Conarroe
Lutz Dille
Pete Doherty
Éliane Excoffier
Daniel & Geo Fuchs
Jim Goldberg
Rafael Goldchain
Tomasz Gudzowaty
Sunil Gupta
Estate of Richard Harrington
Roy Hartling
Dave Heath
Peter Higdon
Vid Ingelevics

Sarah Anne Johnson
Ruth Kaplan
Estate of André Kertész
Mark Kessell
Albert Kish
Anthony Koutras
Laura Letinsky
Estate of Herbert List
Ian MacEachern
MAGNUM Agency
  photographers
E.J. Major
Luis Mallo
Sanaz Mazinani
John Max
Lida Moser
Vincenzo Pietropaolo
Gerald Pisarzowski
Franz Rosenbaum
Alison Rossiter
Mark Ruwedel
David Scopick
Volker Seding

Diana Shearwood
Dona Schwartz
William Gordon Shields
Elizabeth Siegfried
Herb Snitzer
Peter Sramek
Jock Sturges
Gabor Szilasi
Brad Temkin
Jeff Thomas
Michael Torosian
Larry Towell
Pekka Turunen
Alex Webb
Estate of C.D. Woodley
Dawn Woolley
George S. Zimbel
Carl Zimmerman

19th and 20th Century photographers, both known and anonymous, of various genres and types

Reenie Barrow, *Stationea,* 2007
Edition of 5, image size: 23 x 23 inches

BOOTH #314

Robert Burge/20th Century Photographs, Ltd.

315 East 62nd Street
New York, NY 10021

tel: 212-838-4108
fax: 212-838-4390
e-mail: antiques@yaleburge.com
web: www.yaleburge.com

Robert Burge
Ruth Butler
Jerry Jones

Hours: Monday - Friday 10-5
Summer: By Appointment

20th Century Photography, Contemporary Photography, Art Advisory Services

Reenie Barrow
Gaylord Herron
Robert LeBeau
O. Winston Link
Elaine Mayes
D W Mellor
John Woolf

John Woolf, *from Lepidoptera,* 2007
Edition of 25, image Size: 21 x 24 inches

Robert LeBeau, *Nautilus,* 2002
Edition of 15, image Size: 40 x 40 inches

Samantha Everton, *Mind Games*, 2007

Byron McMahon Gallery

88 George Street
Redfern Sydney, NSW 2016, Australia

tel: 61-2-9318-0404
fax: 61-2-9318-0004
e-mail: info@byronmcmahongallery.com.au
web: www.byronmcmahongallery.com.au

Sandra Byron, Director
Peter McMahon, Director
Erin O'Moore, Gallery Manager

Hours: Tuesday - Saturday 11-5

Ansel Adams
Richard Avedon
Judith Ahern
Nick Brandt
Henri Cartier-Bresson
Jeff Carter
Olive Cotton
Max Dupain
Stephen Dupont
Peter Elliston
Samantha Everton
Robert Frank
Paul Freeman
Renato Grome
Horst P. Horst

André Kertész
William Klein
Herman Leonard
Sally Mann
Lee Miller
Lewis Morley
Helmut Newton
Max Pam
Willy Ronis
Sebastião Salgado
Mark Seliger
Vee Speers
Lisa Tomasetti
Ingeborg Tyssen
John Williams

ZONE OF FRICTIONS, SHIFTS AND INFILTRATIONS 1849-2007
an evolutive structure

1

2

3

1 Robert F. Hammerstiel, born 1957, Austrian
Private Stories II, 2005 1/8
Colour photograph on aluminum, framed 125 x 157 centimeters
2 Albert Rudomine, 1892-1975, French
Legs nude study, 1930
Vintage toned black and white gelatin silver print 23.3 x 17.5 centimeters
3 Pierre Jahan, 1909-2003, French
Two half violins, 1942
Vintage black and white gelatin silver print 36.6 x 29.2 centimeters
4 François-Auguste Ravier, 1814-1895, French
Crémieu, tower, 1849
Paper negative 18 x 18 centimeters
5 Noelle Hoeppe, born 1958, French
Blood II, 2001/2006 1/8
Colour photograph on aluminum + diasec, 136 x 100 centimeters

4

5

galerie michèle chomette

24 rue Beaubourg
Paris, 75003, France

tel: 33-1-42-78-05-62
fax: 33-1-42-72-62-05

Michèle Chomette, Owner/Director

Hours: Wednesday - Saturday 2-8
And By Appointment

2007 will have the force of a single proposal -a single exhibition- but one that will be ever-changing, discontinuous, multiform, through an esthetic dialog between history and contemporary developments in photography

---

Exclusive vintage photography collections.
Major Works and Discoveries.

French and International
Contemporary Artists

France 1849-1870
Olympe Aguado
Édouard Baldus
Eugène Cuvelier
V. Dijon
Jean-Jacques Heilmann
Félix Auguste Leclerc
Eugène Mailand
Paul-Émile Miot
Charles Nègre
François-Auguste Ravier
Henri Sauvaire
Adolphe Terris
Félix Thiollier
Louis Vignes

Étienne-Jules Marey

Europe 1920-1950
Bauhaus
Pierre Jahan
Lotte Jacobi
André Kertész
Germaine Krull
Eli Lotar
Albert Renger-Patzsch
Charlotte Rudolph
Albert Rudomine
José Maria Sert
Josef Sudek
Ladislav Sutnar
Willy Zielke
Piet Zwart

after 1970
Arnaud Claass, Fr.
Noelle Hoeppe, Fr.
Jacquelin/Darbelley, Fr.
Guillaume Leingre, Fr.
Guillaume Lemarchal, Fr.
François Méchain, Fr.
Bernard Plossu, Fr.
Jean-Pascal Princiaux, Fr.
Hervé Rabot, Fr.
Jacqueline Salmon, Fr.
Riwan Tromeur, Fr.
Bernar Venet, Fr.

Gilbert Boyer, Que.
Nancy Burson, U.S.
Felten-Massinger, Belg.
Trey Friedman, U.S.
Paolo Gioli, It.
Robert F. Hammerstiel, Aus.
Werner Hannappel, Germ.
Hogan & Amblard, U.S./Swit.
Mikael Levin, U.S./Fr.
Otmar Thormann, Aus./Swed.
Holger Trülzsch, Germ./Fr.

Guillaume Leingre, born 1971, French
Shooting on June 9, 2005, 1/3
by Thierry Gouirriec, Contraste, *Portraitist of France*,
Oloron-Sainte-Marie, Pyrénées Atlantique
Colour photograph, 34 x 42 centimeters

6

Sean Perry, *Event Horizon*
Platinum paladium print

Kate Breakey, *Three Nest*
Hand painted silver gelatin print

Stephen L. Clark Gallery

1101 West Sixth Street
Austin, TX 78703

tel: 512-477-0828
fax: 512-477-0934
e-mail: slcgallery@mac.com
web: www.artnet.com/slclark.html

Steve Clark, Owner
Amber Levis, Gallery Director

Hours: Tuesday - Saturday 10-4
And By Appointment

Contemporary Photography

Frank Armstrong	Nine Francois	Rocky Schenck
Michael P. Berman	Lynn Geesaman	Cathy Spence
Ave Bonar	Graciela Iturbide	Jack Spencer
Kate Breakey	Adam Jahiel	Bob "Daddy-O" Wade
Peter Brown	Robb Kendrick	Rick Williams
Keith Carter	David Michael Kennedy	Laura Wilson
Diana Dopson	O. Rufus Lovett	Geoff Winningham
Jay Dusard	Sean Perry	Bill Wittliff
James Evans	Josephine Sacabo	Lance Letscher

Jack Spencer, *Hedgerows*
Mixed media

André Kertész, *Chez Mondrian,* 1926

Maggie Taylor, *These Strange Adventures,* 2006

John Cleary Gallery

2635 Colquitt
Houston, TX 77098

tel: 713-524-5070
e-mail: info@johnclearygallery.com
web: www.johnclearygallery.com

John Cleary
Catherine Couturier

Hours: Tuesday - Saturday 10-5

John Cleary Gallery, Houston's premiere gallery dedicated to photograph, shows classic photography masters such as André Kertész, Henri Cartier-Bresson and Robert Doisneau as well as contemporary artists such as Maggie Taylor and David Fokos. The gallery also sells a wide range of rare and vintage books, and publications by many of today's best-known contemporary artists.

Stanko Abadzic
Jeffrey Becom
Ruth Bernhard
Jayne Hinds Bidaut
Margaret Bourke-White
Bill Brandt
Manuel Alvarez Bravo
Dan Burkholder
Camera Work
Marty Carden
Henri Cartier-Bresson
Larry Clark
Jeffrey Conley
Charles Cramer
Robert Doisneau
Richard Drury
Martin Elkort

Lisa Tyson Ennis
David Fokos
Jefferson Hayman
Thurston Hopkins
Henry Horenstein
Earlie Hudnall
George Hurrell
Adam Jahiel
Michael Kenna
André Kertész
Dorothea Lange
Great Life Photographers
Marshall Noice
Ruth Orkin
Bill Perlmutter
Brent Phelps
The Photo League

Grace Robertson
Willy Ronis
Arthur Rothstein
Eva Rubinstein
Pentti Sammallahti
Joe Schwartz
Rodney Smith
Maggie Taylor
George Tice
Juliet Van Otteren
Tenesh Webber
Eudora Welty
John Wimberley
Marion Post Wolcott
George Zimbel
Ion Zupcu

Daido Moriyama, *How To Create a Beautiful Picture 6: Tights in Shimotakaido*, 1987

Stephen Cohen Gallery, Inc.

7358 Beverly Boulevard
Los Angeles, CA 90036

tel: 323-937-5525
fax: 323-937-5523
e-mail: info@stephencohengallery.com
web: www.stephencohengallery.com

Stephen Cohen, Owner
Beverly Feldman, Gallery Director
Rick Perez, Assistant Director
Jean-Paul Biondi, Gallery Manager
Danny Jauregui, Gallery Assistant

Hours: Tuesday - Saturday 11-6

The Stephen Cohen Gallery was opened in 1992 and since it's inception, the Gallery has exhibited vintage and contemporary photography and photo-based art from the United States, Europe and South America.

Diane Arbus	Brian Finke	Ken Ohara
Kiichi Asano	Anthony Friedkin	Suzanne Opton
Nick Brandt	Lynn Geesaman	Luis González Palma
Horace Bristol	Judy Gelles	Arthur Siegel
Peter Brown	Josef Hoflehner	Tracey Snelling
Carl Chiarenza	Pieter Hugo	Josef Sudek
Larry Clark	Thomas Kellner	Edmund Teske
Livia Corona	Maureen Lambray	Jonathan Torgovnik
John Davies	Tony Mendoza	Tseng Kwong Chi
Louis Faurer	Daido Moriyama	Weegee
Harold Feinstein	Viggo Mortensen	Bill Witt
Larry Fink	Lori Nix	Ida Wyman

Berenice Abbott, *Nightview,* New York, 1932

Commerce Graphics Ltd., Inc.

506 East 74th Street
New York, NY 10021

tel: 212-517-7648
fax: 212-517-7649
e-mail: info@commercegraphics.com

Ron Kurtz, President
Cindy Johnson, Director
Natalie Evans, Associate Director

Hours: Tuesday - Friday 10-5
Monday By Appointment

Twentieth Century Master Photography

Commerce Graphics holds the Estate of Berenice Abbott and exclusive representation of Arnold Newman.

Artists
Berenice Abbott
Arnold Newman

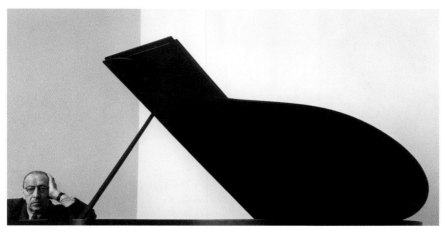

Arnold Newman, *Igor Stravinsky,* New York City, 1946

Francois Kollar, *Double-Impression of the Eiffel Tower, Paris,* c.1931
Vintage silver print

Contemporary Works / Vintage Works, Ltd.

258 Inverness Circle
Chalfont, PA 18914

tel: 215-822-5662
fax: 215-822-8003
e-mail: info@vintageworks.net
web: www.vintageworks.net
www.contemporaryworks.net
www.iphotocentral.com

Alex Novak
Marthe Smith

Hours: By Appointment

**Fine Vintage 19th, 20th and 21st Century Photography
by American, English and European Masters**

Artists Exhibited

Berenice Abbott
Laure Albin-Guillot
Eugene Atget
Edouard Baldus
Paul Berthier
Adolphe Bertsch
Ilsa Bing
Bisson Freres
Lewis Baltz
Marcel Bovis
Edouard Boubat
Brassaï
Adolphe Braun
Manuel Alvarez Bravo
Harry Callahan
Julia M. Cameron
Lewis Carroll
Henri Cartier-Bresson
Desire Charnay
Charles Clifford
Eugene Cuvelier
Louis De Clercq
Baron Adolf De Meyer
Robert Doisneau
Jean Dreville
Frantisek Drtikol
Maxime Du Camp
Thomas Eakins

Walker Evans
Roger Fenton
Robert Frank
Hill & Adamson
Paul Horst
Hugo & Vacquerie
Alfred Cheney Johnston
André Kertész
Francois Kollar
Germaine Krull
Col. Jean-Charles Langlois
Jacques-Henri Lartigue
Clarence John Laughlin
Gustave Le Gray
Helen Levitt
Henri Le Secq
Man Ray
Marcel Marien
Charles Marville
Leon Eugene Mehedin
Barbara Morgan
William Mortensen
Dr. John Murray
Charles Negre
Dorothy Norman
Irving Penn
Constant Puyo
Louis Robert
Willy Ronis

Auguste Salzmann
Sherill Schell
W. Eugene Smith
Southworth & Hawes
Edward Steichen
Otto Steinert
Alfred Stieglitz
Louis Stoumen
Josef Sudek
Adolphe Terris
Captain Linnaeus Tripe
Julien Vallou de Villeneuve
Geza Vandor
Max Waldman
Carleton Watkins
Sabine Weiss
Brett Weston
Clarence White
Joel-Peter Witkin.

Artists Represented

Stanko Abadzic
Marcus Doyle
Lisa Holden
Joel D. Levinson
Krzysztof Pruszkowski
Charlie Schreiner
Jerry Spagnoli
Arthur Tress

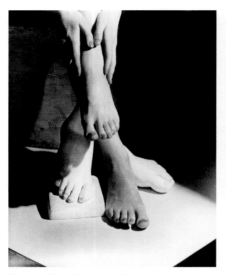

Horst Paul Horst, *Barefoot*, 1936
Vintage silver print

Edward Steichen, *Marion Morehouse in Cheruit Gown*, 1927
Vintage silver print

Marcus Doyle, *Urban Sport 1 (Single Post)*, 2004/2007
Chromogenic print

Lisa Holden, *Blue Cape*, 2003/2005
Chromogenic print on Fuji Crystal Archive in Diasec mount

Henry Wessel, *Pennsylvania*, 1968
Gelatin silver print, 24 x 20 inches

Charles Cowles Gallery

537 West 24th Street
New York, NY 10011

tel: 212-741-8999
fax: 212-741-6222
e-mail: info@cowlesgallery.com
web: www.cowlesgallery.com

Represented Photographers
José Manuel Ballester
Edward Burtynsky
John Divola
Mona Kuhn
Henry Wessel

Mona Kuhn, *Reflecting*, 2006
Chromogenic print, 50 x 50 inches, edition of 3

Frantisek Drtikol, *Nude,* 1920s later print
Silver print, 30.5 x 23 centimeters, unsigned

Czech Center of Photography

Hybernska 7a
Praha 1, 110 00, Czech Republic

tel: 420-296-522-284
fax: 420-296-522-259
e-mail: ccf@volny.cz
web: www.greisen.cz

Jiri Jaskmanicky, Owner

Hours: 11-6 daily

CCF is a private institute, founded in 1994. It organizes exhibition projects, collecting activities, publishes photographical books and trades photography. CCF is the only institute in the Czech Republic, which systematically promotes art photography, that is classical as well as contemporary all the way to the youngest authors. It represents exclusively classic authors (Petr Helbich, Tibor Honty, Josef Bartuska, Antonin Gribovsky, Ladislav Postupa,...) and contemporary authors (Matus Toth, Viktor Kopasz, Vaclav Jirasek, etc.)

Josef Bartuska	Jaromir Funke
Karel Otto Hruby	Vilem Reichmann
Ladislav Emil Berka	Rudolf Gotsche
Vaclav Jirasek	Jaroslav Rössler
Jindrich Brok	Antonin Gribovsky
Viktor Kopasz	Drahomir Josef Ruzicka
Vladimír Jindrich Bufka	Miroslav Hak
Karel Ludwig	Jan Saudek
Frantisek Drtikol	Alexander Hammid
Jan Lauschmann	Bohumil Stastny
Josef Ehm	Petr Helbich
Jan Lukas	Josef Sudek
Zdenko Fejfar	Tibor Honty
Vladimir Neubert	Jan Svoboda

Gary Schneider, *Mask*, 1999
Pigmented ink on stretched canvas and framed, 52 ¹/₂ x 40 inches

Stephen Daiter Gallery /
Daiter Contemporary

311 West Superior Street, # 404/408
Chicago, IL 60610

tel: 312-787-3350
fax: 312-787-3354
e-mail: info@stephendaitergallery.com
web: www.stephendaitergallery.com

Stephen Daiter
Paul Berlanga
Michael Welch

Hours: Wednesday - Friday 11-6
And By Appointment

20th and 21st Century European and American Avant-Garde and Documentary Photographs.
Photography from School of Design in Chicago, Photo League, New York School, Bauhaus,
and Farm Security Administration.

20th Century	**School of Design**	**Contemporary**
Bill Brandt	Harry Callahan	Paul D'Amato
Estate of Josef Breitenbach	Barbara Crane	Ben Gest
Wynn Bullock	Estate of Robert Erickson	John Gossage
Henri Cartier-Bresson	Yasuhiro Ishimoto	Susan Meiselas
Rod Cook	Joseph Jachna	Martin Parr
Willem Diepraam	Kenneth Josephson	Gary Schneider
Morris Engel	Gyorgy Kepes	Terri Weifenbach
Walker Evans	Estate of Nathan Lerner	
Jaromir Funke	Laszlo Moholy-Nagy	
Lewis Hine	Marvin Newman	
André Kertész	Arthur Siegel	
Helen Levitt	Art Sinsabaugh	
Clarence John Laughlin	Aaron Siskind	
Leon Levinstein	Joseph Sterling	
Estate of Herbert List		
Dora Maar		
Ralph Eugene Meatyard		
Wayne Miller		
Art Shay		
W. Eugene Smith		
Frederick Sommer		
Josef Sudek		
Edmund Teske		
Minor White		

Wouter Deruytter, *Fifth Avenue and 56th Street (Asprey #2), NYC*, 2003

Michael Prince, *Cloverleaf, Shanghai, China*, 2006

David Gallery

5797 Washington Blvd.
Culver City, CA 90232

tel: 323-939-9069
fax: 323-939-9079
e-mail: info@davidgallery.net
web: www.davidgallery.net

David Barenholtz
Joshua Holzmann

Hours: Tuesday - Saturday 11-6

David Gallery (formerly APEX Fine Art) has taken the fundamentals and strengths of its former gallery and expanded in size and scope to focus on masters of contemporary photography. David Gallery exhibits a wide range of work with an emphasis on architectural and large format photography and photojournalism.

William Albert Allard
Anderson & Low
Eve Arnold
Sid Avery
Harry Benson
Margaret Bourke-White
Marilyn Bridges
Jodi Cobb
Loomis Dean
Wouter Deruytter
John Dominis
Alfred Eisenstaedt
Andreas Feininger
Brandon Herman
Kobe Israel

Neil Leifer
John Loengard
Ralph Morse
Carl Mydans
Bill Perlmutter
Michael Prince
Amalie Rothschild
Michal Safdie
Howard Schatz
Mark Shaw
Larry Snider
Peter Stackpole
Alexey Titarenko
Bob Willoughby
Stephen Wilkes

Ansel Adams, *The Sheer Face of Half Dome,* From the *Winter Sports in Yosemite Album,* c. 1931
Vintage gelatin silver print

Michael Dawson Gallery

535 North Larchmont Boulevard
Los Angeles, CA 90004

tel: 323-469-2186
fax: 323-469-9553
e-mail: info@michaeldawsongallery.com
web: www.michaeldawsongallery.com

Michael Dawson

Hours: Wednesday - Saturday 10-5

Specializing in nineteenth and twentieth century American photography with an emphasis on vintage and contemporary work from California and the Southwest. We also maintain an inventory of rare photographic books.

Ansel Adams
Ruth Bernhard
Horace Bristol
Kaucyila Brooke
Will Connell
Edward Curtis
William Dassonville
Judy Dater
Scott Davis
Robert Frank
Yuichi Hibi

André Kertész
Claudia Kunin
Christopher Landis
Gary Leonard
Charles Lummis
C. Cameron Macauley
Daido Moriyama
Eadweard Muybridge
Sonya Noskowiak
Ira Nowinski
Rondal Partridge

Charles Phoenix Archive
Ken Rosenthal
A.J. Russell
Robert Sheer
Will Soule
Roger Vail
Rudy Vanderlans
Adam Clark Vroman
Edward Weston
Max Yavno

Ansel Adams, *Merced River, Yosemite Valley,* From the *Winter Sports in Yosemite Album,* c. 1931
Vintage gelatin silver print

Margaret Bourke-White, *Toward the Sun*, c. 1929
Vintage gelatin silver print

Peyser & Patzig, *Chrysler Building*, 1929
Vintage gelatin silver print

Keith de Lellis Gallery

Mailing address until June 2007
141 E 88th Street, Apt 4A
New York, NY 10128
tel: 212-410-5440
tel: 917-533-4964

New address June 2007
1045 Madison Avenue
New York, NY 10075
tel: 212-327-1482
fax: 212-327-1492
e-mail: keith@keithdelellisgallery.com
web: www.keithdelellisgallery.com

Keith de Lellis, Director

Hours: Tuesday - Friday 10-6, Saturday 11-5

Photographs by American and European photographers of the 20th century including vintage Italian photography, fashion, industrial, New York School, and 19th century spirit photography. Also in inventory: photo-journalism, advertising photography, modernist photography, and photographs of the Clarence H. White School. Other subjects include nudes, sports, social documentary, and travel photography.

Berenice Abbott	Mario Finocchiaro	Irving Penn
Richard Avedon	Mario Giacomelli	George Platt Lynes
Ralph Bartholomew	Baron Wilhelm von Gloeden	Edward Quigley
Cecil Beaton	Antoinette Hervey	Man Ray
Benedetta Bonichi	Lejaren Hiller	Flip Schulke
Margaret Bourke-White	Paul Himmel	Mark Shaw
Giuseppe Bruno	Lewis Hine	Bernard Shea Horne
Esther Bubley	George Hoyningen-Huene	Emilio Sommariva
Augusto Cantamessa	Simpson Kalisher	Ema Spencer
Mario Carrieri	Gertrude Kasebier	Edward Steichen
Henri Cartier-Bresson	Jan Lukas	Rolf Tietgens
Mario Cattaneo	Daniel Masclet	Claude Tolmer
Ed Clark	Nino Migliori	Doris Ulmann
Harold Haliday Costain	Wayne F. Miller	Alfredo Valente
Gordon Coster	Leonard Misonne	Walery
Louise Dahl-Wolfe	Benn Mitchell	Weegee
Mario De Biasi	Marvin E. Newman	Clarence H. White
Loomis Dean	PAJAMA	Bob Willoughby
Robert Doisneau	Gordon Parks	Paul Woolf

Gregory Conniff, *Yalobusha County, Mississippi*, 2004

Candace Dwan Gallery

24 West 57th Street #503
New York, NY 10019
tel: 212-315-0065
fax: 212-315-2220
e-mail: email@candacedwan.com
web: www.candacedwan.com

Second location:
27 Katonah Avenue
Katonah, New York 10536
tel/fax: 914-232-3966
e-mail: email@candacedwan.com

Candace Dwan, Director
Alexa Coyne, Gallery Manager, Katonah
Christine Stamas, Gallery Manager, New York

Hours: Tuesday - Saturday 11-6

Slim Aarons
Edouard Boubat
Margaret Bourke-White
Brassaï
Denis Brihat
Gregory Conniff
Harold Edgerton
Afred Eisenstaedt
Harold Feinstein
Chip Forelli

William Garnett
Stanley Greenberg
Henry Horenstein
Rolfe Horn
Adam Jahiel
Stuart Klipper
Bogdan Konopka
O. Winston Link
Raymond Meeks

Olivier Meriel
Dr. Albert Richards
Pentti Sammallahti
Edward Steichen
Tony Stromberg
George Tice
Sabine Weiss
Janet Woodcock
Reid Yalom

Pentti Sammallahti, *Swayambhunath, Nepal, 1994*

Robert & Shana ParkeHarrison, *Mourning Cloak,* 2006

Julie Blackmon, *Camouflage*, 2006

Catherine Edelman Gallery

300 West Superior Street, Lower Level
Chicago, IL 60610

tel: 312-266-2350
fax: 312-266-1967
e-mail: catherine@edelmangallery.com
web: www.edelmangallery.com

Catherine Edelman, Director
Melanie Pankau, Assistant Director
Marissa Baker, Preparator

Hours: Tuesday - Saturday 10-5:30

The gallery specializes in Contemporary Photography

Shelby Lee Adams	Michelle Keim	Josephine Sacabo
Roger Ballen	Michael Kenna	Gregory Scott
Tom Baril	Herman Leonard	Rocky Schenck
Julie Blackmon	O. Winston Link	Jack Spencer
Keith Carter	Deborah Luster	Ruth Thorne-Thomsen
Clark & Pougnaud	Cecil McDonald Jr.	Ron van Dongen
Bruce Davidson	Richard Misrach	Alex Webb
Carlos Diaz	Andrea Modica	Joel-Peter Witkin
Elizabeth Ernst	Abelardo Morell	Jeffrey Wolin
Dan Estabrook	Olivia Parker	
Terry Evans	Melissa Ann Pinney	
Lynn Geesaman	David Plowden	
David Graham	Holly Roberts	

Clark & Pougnaud, *Alexandra et Sorine*, 2004

Maxime DuCamp, *Isamboul, Egypt,* 1852
Calotype

Gary Edwards Gallery

1711 Connecticut Avenue, NW
Washington, DC 20009

tel: 301-524-0900
e-mail: garymedwards@mac.com

Gary Edwards, Director

Hours: Monday - Friday 10-4

19th and 20th Century Photographs

The gallery specializes in 19th century travel photographs, 20th century historic photographs, modern masters, a limited number of contemporary photographers from Russia, Japan and the United States, and rare vintage prints concerning space exploration.

American vernacular	Alphonse Mucha
Ernest Benecke	NASA
Felix Bonfils	Misako Oba
Samuel Bourne	Albert Rudomine
Dmitri Constantine	Igor Savchenko
Ernst Fuhrmann	Boris Smelov
Lotte Jacobi	W.J. Stillman
Bertha Jaques	Louis Comfort Tiffany
Juan Laurent	Alexei Titarenko
Man Ray	Francesca Woodman
Robert McCabe	Alexander Zhitomirsky

Misako Oba, *They Might Amputate My Pinkie #1*, 2006
From the series Self Portraits since 1994

Etherton Gallery

135 South 6th Avenue
Tucson, AZ 85701

tel: 520-624-7370
fax: 520-792-4569
e-mail: info@ethertongallery.com
web: www.ethertongallery.com

Terry Etherton, President
Hannah Glasston, Gallery Director
Daphne Srinivasan, Publicist
Dawne Osborne, Registrar

Hours: Tuesday - Saturday 11-5, Thursday until 7
And By Appointment

For 25 years Etherton Gallery has been a destination for photography collectors in the Southwest. Housed in the historic Odd Fellows Hall in downtown Tucson, Arizona, the gallery's specialty lies in its extensive inventory of vintage, classic, and contemporary photography. Terry Etherton is an accredited member of The American Society of Appraisers and is available to collectors as a consultant and absent bidder.

Ansel Adams	Jack Dykinga	Wright Morris
Albert Arthur Allen	Dr. Harold Edgerton	Eadweard Muybridge
Tim Archibald	Elliott Erwitt	Michael O'Neill
Dick Arentz	Walker Evans	Frederick Sommer
William Bell	Robert Frank	Timothy O'Sullivan
Michael Berman	Flor Garduño	Frank Rinehart
Manuel Alvarez Bravo	Ralph Gibson	Holly Roberts
Kate Breakey	Emmet Gowin	Ken Rosenthal
Wynn Bullock	Adriel Heisey	Rocky Schenck
Debra Bloomfield	John Hillers	Aaron Siskind
Christopher Burkett	Graciela Iturbide	W. Eugene Smith
Debbie Fleming Caffery	William Henry Jackson	Jock Sturges
Harry Callahan	Adam Jahiel	Dr. Max Thorek
Camerawork	André Kertész	Alex Webb
Paul Caponigro	Mark Klett	Brett Weston
Keith Carter	O. Winston Link	Minor White
Linda Connor	Danny Lyon	Gordon Whitten
Edward S. Curtis	Richard Misrach	Joel-Peter Witkin
Jay Dusard	Karl Moon	

Joel-Peter Witkin, *Abundance, Prague*, 1997
Unique encaustic over hand-colored gelatin silver print, with artist-designed frame, 45 ¹/₂ x 37 ¹/₂ inches

© Willy Ronis, *Joueur de Pétanque, Aubagne*, 1947

© Victoria Ryan, *Ancient Oaks*, 2006

Kathleen Ewing Gallery

New Address
1767 P Street, NW, Suite 3
Washington, DC 20036

tel: 202-328-0955
fax: 202-462-1019
e-mail: ewingal@aol.com
web: www.kathleenewinggallery.com

Kathleen Ewing, Director
Charlotte Vazquez, Assistant Director
JoAnne Ewing, Assistant to the Director
Ingrid Yan, Gallery Assistant

Hours: Wednesday - Saturday 11-6
And By Appointment

Contemporary & Vintage Photography, and Photo-based Art

20th Century
Karl Blossfeldt
A. Aubrey Bodine Estate
Esther Bubley
Willy Ronis
August Sander
James Van Der Zee
Marion Post Wolcott

Contemporary Photographers
Sam Abell
David Allison
Anderson & Low
Allen Appel
Robert W. Bazemore, Jr.
Bruce Barnbaum
Jeanne Birdsall
Phil Borges
Stuart M. Brafman
Christopher Burkett
Joe Cameron
Diane Cook
Libby Cullen
Frank DiPerna
Michael Eastman
Janos Enyedi
Macduff Everton
Don Fear
Kate Freedberg
Janet Fries
John Grant
Adriel Heisey
Henry Horenstein
Allan Janus
Len Jenshel

Martin Kollar
Frank Lavelle
Stephen Lawson
Alex MacLean
Fred Maroon
Bruce McKaig
Meredith McKinney
Darrow Montgomery
Joan Myers
Rajesh Nair
Kendall Nelson
Karla G. Nicholson
Hiroshi Osaka
Mark Power
Rosamond Purcell
John Reef
Robert Richardson
Grace Robertson
Victoria Ryan
Judy Sanchez
Floyd Segel
Claudia Smigrod
Steve Szabo
Benjamin C. Tankersley
Anna Tomczak
Eileen Toumanoff
Claudio Vazquez

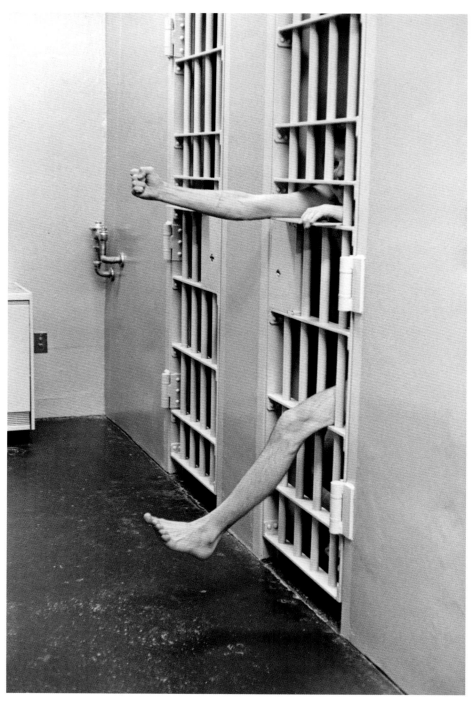

Henri Cartier-Bresson, *Prisoner, New Jersey*, 1974
Vintage silver print, 23 x 15.2 centimeters, (9 x 6 inches)

Galerie Johannes Faber

Brahmsplatz 7
Vienna, 1040, Austria

tel/fax: 43-1-505-75-18
e-mail: office@jmcfaber.at
web: www.jmcfaber.at

Johannes Faber
Michaela Hüttner

Hours: Tuesday - Friday 2-6, Saturday 11-5
And By Appointment

20th Century Vintage & Contemporary Photographs

We are specialized in Austrian and Czech as well as American and European Classic Modern.

Dick Arentz	Heinrich Kuehn	Alexander Rodchenko
Cecil Beaton	Will McBride	Jaroslav Roessler
Lou Bonin-Tchimoukoff	Henry Moore	Drahomir Ruzicka
Keith Carter	Inge Morath	Jan Saudek
Henri Cartier-Bresson	Helmut Newton	Rudolf Schwarzkogler
Robert Doisneau	Hermann Nitsch	Carl Struewe
Frantisek Drtikol	John Pfahl	Jock Sturges
William Eggleston	Pablo Picasso	Josef Sudek
Trude Fleischmann	Edward Quigley	Anton Josef Trcka
Robert Frank	Arnulf Rainer	Weegee
Ernst Haas	Man Ray	Robert Zahornicky
Philippe Halsman	Vilem Reichmann	
André Kertész	Wolfgang Reichmann	See more artists on
Rudolf Koppitz	Albert Renger-Patzsch	our website.

MARK LAITA
Created Equal

Marine/War Veteran, 2002/2004

Polygamist with Wives/Pimp with Prostitutes, 2004/2003

BOOTH #105

Fahey/Klein Gallery

148 North La Brea Avenue
Los Angeles, CA 90036

tel: 323-934-2250
fax: 323-934-4243
e-mail: fkg@earthlink.net
web: www.faheykleingallery.com

David Fahey, Co-owner
Ken Devlin, Co-owner
James Gilbert, Associate Director
Gisele Schmidt, Associate Director
Stephen Heer, Registrar

Hours: Tuesday - Saturday 10-6

20th Century Vintage and Contemporary Photography
Photojournalism/Reportage Photography

Shelby Lee Adams
David Bailey
Roger Ballen
Peter Beard
Erwin Blumenfeld
Alvin Booth
Bill Brandt
Brassai
Manuel Alvarez Bravo
Henri Cartier-Bresson
Michal Chelbin
William Claxton
Robert Coburn
David Drebin
John Filo
Robert Frank
Flor Garduno
Greg Gorman
Lauren Greenfield
Horst P. Horst

Frank Horvat
Nadav Kander
Geof Kern
André Kertész
William Klein
David LaChapelle
Mark Laita
Annie Leibovitz
Herman Leonard
Herbert List
Danny Lyon
Man Ray
Robert Mapplethorpe
Mary Ellen Mark
Jim Marshall
Robert Maxwell
Duane Michals
Nickolas Muray
James Nachtwey
Helmut Newton

Paul Outerbridge
Irving Penn
Rankin
Leni Riefenstahl
Herb Ritts
Sebastião Salgado
Steve Schapiro
Mark Seliger
Melvin Sokolsky
Rodney Smith
Bert Stern
Phil Stern
Jock Sturges
Nick Ut
Bruce Weber
Nathaniel Welch
Edward Weston
Garry Winogrand
Joel-Peter Witkin

Weegee, *Heat Spell, May 23, 1941*
© Weegee / International Center of Photography

Henry Feldstein

PO Box 398
Forest Hills, NY 11375

tel: 718-544-3002
fax: 718-544-7139
e-mail: henryfe@ix.netcom.com

Henry Feldstein, Director

Hours: By Appointment

BOOTH #213

**19th and 20th Century Photographs
and Rare Photographic Literature**

We specialize in in photographs by Weegee and maintain a large selection of vintage photographs of Bettie Page.

Berenice Abbott	Henri Cartier-Bresson	Albert Renger-Patzsch
Ansel Adams	Larry Clark	Drahomir Ruzicka
Jose Alemany	Rudolf Eickemeyer	Aaron Siskind
Albert Arthur Allen	Elliot Erwitt	W. Eugene Smith
Elmer Batters	Walker Evans	Edward Steichen
Cecil Beaton	Mario Giacomelli	Ralph Steiner
Ruth Bernhard	Lena Scott Harris	Karl Struss
Ilse Bing	Fritz Henle	Josef Sudek
A. Aubrey Bodine	André Kertész	Weegee
Bill Brandt	Germaine Krull	Brett Weston
Brassaï	J.H. Lartigue	Edward Weston
Manuel Alvarez Bravo	William Mortensen	Garry Winogrand
Hugo Brehme	P.H. Oelman	Max Yavno
Wynn Bullock	Bettie Page	
Harry Callahan	Eliot Porter	

Sebastião Salgado, *Iceberg between Paulet Island & the Shetlands Islands, Antarctica,* 2005. From the series *Genesis*

Sebastião Salgado, *Chinstrap Penguins (Pygoscelis Antartica), Deception Island, Antarctica,* 2005. From the series *Genesis*

Peter Fetterman Gallery

2525 Michigan Avenue, #A7
Santa Monica, CA 90404

tel: 310-453-6463
fax: 310-453-6959
e-mail: info@peterfetterman.com
web: www.peterfetterman.com

Peter Fetterman, Owner & Director
Sam Lee, Director
Marco Paez, Assistant Director

Hours: Tuesday - Saturday 10-6

We carry one of the largest inventories of classic 20th century photography on the west coast.

Berenice Abbott	William Klein
Jesse Alexander	Laszlo Layton
Eugène Atget	Arthur Leipzig
Lillian Bassman	Helen Levitt
Ruth Bernhard	O. Winston Link
Brigitte Carnochan	Jacques Lowe
Cornell Capa	Steve McCurry
Robert Capa	Byung Hun Min
Paul Caponigro	Arnold Newman
Henri Cartier-Bresson	David Plowden
Elliott Erwitt	Grace Robertson
Martine Franck	Willy Ronis
Mario Giacomelli	Sebastião Salgado
Chester Higgins, Jr.	Jerry Schatzberg
Thurston Hopkins	John Szarkowski
Horst P. Horst	George Tice
Don Hunstein	Ron Van Dongen
André Kertész	Fred Zinnemann

Torrance York, *N41º46.562' W073º50.901' 11/23/03 429 ft., (Melville Road)*, 2005
C print, 28 x 28 inches, Edition of 10

Wm. Floyd

PO Box 1628 Lenox Hill Station
New York, NY 10021

tel: 212-365-0658
e-mail: wmfloyd@verizon.net
web: www.floydgallery.com

William L. Floyd
Lyle Cavanaugh

Hours: By Appointment

20th Century and Contemporary Photographs

Works by
A. Aubrey Bodine
Geoff Carter
William Christenberry
Lynn Davis
Elena Dorfman
Deborah Frankel
Adam Fuss
David H. Gibson
Emmet Gowin
Horst P. Horst
Birney Imes
Dusan Keim
Fred G. Korth
Michelle Luke
Sally Mann
W. Mantz
McDermott & McGough
Helmut Newton
Charles Pratt
William Rittase

Representing
Bill Armstrong
France Bourely
Jack Bradley
David Deal
Keoki Flagg
Tony Law
Charles Lindsay
Malcolm Lightner
Paul Meleschnig
Robert A. Schaefer, Jr.
Marc Valesella
Torrance York

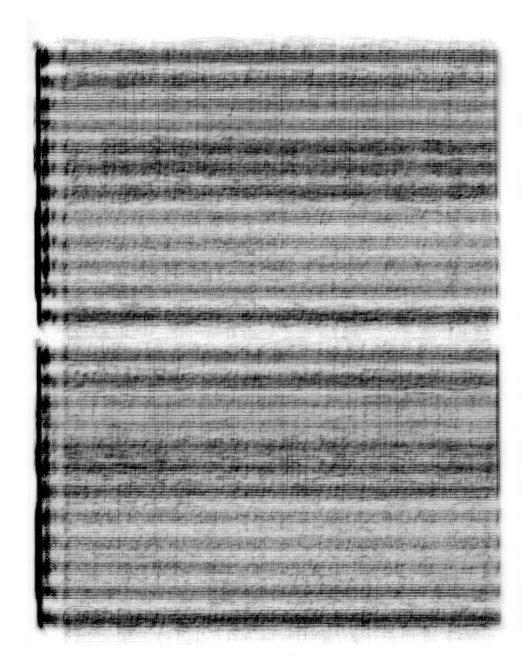

Idris Khan, *Mozart... Requiem (Venice 2005)*, 2006

Fraenkel Gallery

49 Geary Street
San Francisco, CA 94108

tel: 415-981-2661
fax: 415-981-4014
e-mail: mail@fraenkelgallery.com
web: www.fraenkelgallery.com

Jeffrey Fraenkel, President
Frish Brandt, Director
Elizabeth Chiles, Associate Director

Hours: Tuesday - Friday 10:30-5:30, Saturday 11-5

Modern Art Specializing in Photographs

Robert Adams
Diane Arbus
Eugène Atget
Richard Avedon
Bernd & Hilla Becher
E.J. Bellocq
Harry Callahan
Chuck Close
Bill Dane
Walker Evans
Robert Frank
Lee Friedlander
Adam Fuss
Gilbert & George
Nan Goldin
Katy Grannan
John Gutmann

Peter Hujar
Idris Khan
Helen Levitt
Sol LeWitt
Man Ray
Ralph Eugene Meatyard
Richard Misrach
Eadweard Muybridge
Nicholas Nixon
Paul Outerbridge
Irving Penn
August Sander
Hiroshi Sugimoto
Carleton E. Watkins
Edward Weston
Garry Winogrand
and others

Norman Parkinson, *Golfing Le Touquet*, 1939
Silver gelatin print, 16 x 12 inches, © Norman Parkinson Archive, London

Eric Franck Fine Art

Unit 8010, 1st floor
61 Willow Walk
London, SE1 5SF, UK

tel: 44-207-394 9743
fax: 44-207-394 1956
e-mail: e.franck@btclick.com

Eric Franck
Elizabeth Smith
Judith Platte

Hours: By Appointment

Founded in 1982, Eric Franck Fine Art was first based in Geneva where it operated as Galerie
Eric Franck until 1994. From 1990 to 2000, it was also based in Berlin as Galerie Franck & Schulte,
and since then has been in London. Eric Franck specialises in 20th century and contemporary
photography and photographic literature. Since 2006 he represents the Norman Parkinson Archive
with Elizabeth Smith.

Kiichi Asano
Geraldo de Barros
Henri Cartier-Bresson
Alvin Langdon Coburn
William Eggleston
Martine Franck
Hana Jakrlova
Josef Koudelka
Norman Parkinson
Willy Rizzo
Jindrich Streit

Francois Kollar, 1930
Vintage silver print

Gallery 19/21

9 Little Harbor Road
Guilford, CT 06437

tel: 203-453-6215
fax: 203-453-5612
e-mail: gallery19th21st@aol.com
web: gallery19th21st.free.fr

Florence Pénault

Hours: By Appointment

European and American Vintage Photographs from the 19th and 20th Century, as well as Contemporary Artists

19th century
Edouard-Denis Baldus
Bisson Frères
Jean-Baptiste Frénet
Gustave Le Gray
Charles Nègre

20th century
Berenice Abbott
Eugène Atget
Edouard Boubat
Brassaï
Henri Cartier-Bresson
Blanc & Demilly
Robert Doisneau
Frantisek Drtikol
Jaromir Funke
Mario Giacomelli
Victor Guidalevitch
Raoul Hausmann
Lotte Jacobi
Kertész
Francois Kollar
Rudolf Koppitz
Germaine Krull
Jacques-Henri Lartigue
Man Ray
Willy Ronis
Lucia Moholy
André Steiner
Josef Sudek
Paul Wolff

Contemporary
Martha Casanave
Sean Kernan
Anne Leigniel
Tina Mérandon
William Ropp
Ryuijie
Guillaume Zuili
Yutaka Yamamoto

Edward Steichen, Im Memoriam, 1904
Gum bichromate over platinum print, 47.5 x 38.5 centimeters
Signed and dated twice upper left: « STEICHEN MDCCCV »
Titled on the back « Memoriam »

Galerie 1900/2000

8 rue Bonaparte
Paris, 75006, France

tel: 33-1-43-25-84-20
fax: 33-1-46-34-74-52
e-mail: dfleiss@galerie1900-2000.com
web: www.galerie1900-2000.com

David Fleiss
Marcel Fleiss
Eleonore Malingue (Contact in New York)

Hours: Monday - Saturday 10-12:30 & 2-7

Marcel Fleiss opened his first gallery in 1972, encouraged by his friend Man Ray, with an exhibition of forty of the artist's rayograms. Since then and from 1981 at the Galerie 1900-2000, he organized more than 150 exhibitions. Since 1991, his son David has developed among others the photography department.

Eugene Atget
Hans Bellmer
Gaston Bertin
Jacques André Boiffard
Brassaï
Henri Cartier Bresson
Robert Doisneau
Frantisek Drtikol
Florence Henri
Germaine Krull
Dora Maar
Man Ray
Pierre Molinier
Maurice Tabard
Dr Paul Wolf
Wols

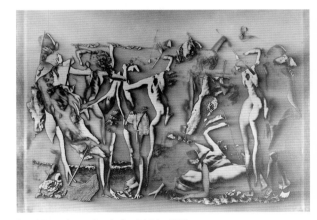

Raoul Ubac, *Le combat de Penthésilée*, 1938
Vintage silver print, 18.3 x 24 centimeters
Signed, dated and titled on the back

JoAnn Verburg, *Olive Trees, Looking Up*, 2003
Chromogenic print, 40 x 56 inches

Ruth Bernhard, *Perspective II*, 1967
Gelatin silver print

G. Gibson Gallery

300 South Washington Street
Seattle, WA 98104

tel: 206-587-4033
fax: 206-587-5751
e-mail: gail@ggibsongallery.com
web: www.ggibsongallery.com

Gail Gibson
Claudia Vernia
K.C. Potter de Haan

Hours: Tuesday - Friday 11-5:30
Saturday 11-5

The G. Gibson Gallery opened in Seattle, Washington in August, 1991. The gallery exhibits contemporary painting, sculpture and installations, works on paper, and continues an emphasis on mid-20th century and contemporary fine art photography. We are also members of the Seattle Art Dealers Association.

Berenice Abbott	John Divola	Mickey Pallas
Hector Acebes	John Dugdale	Olivia Parker
Ansel Adams	Walker Evans	Beverly Rayner
Diane Arbus	Debra Goldman	Herb Ritts
Steven Berardelli	Graciela Iturbide	Carol Sawyer
Ruth Bernhard	Bill Jacobson	Laurel Schultz
Julie Blackmon	John Jenkins III	Susan Seubert
Nealy Blau	Eirik Johnson	Aaron Siskind
Manuel Alvarez Bravo	Michael Kenna	Iain Stewart
Wynn Bullock	Doug Keyes	Takatomo Usui
Linda Butler	Heidi Kirkpatrick	JoAnn Verburg
Debbie Fleming Caffery	Mona Kuhn	Ron van Dongen
Larry Calkins	Jacques-Henri Lartigue	Eva Skold Westerlind
Camera Work Gravures	Helen Levitt	Brett Weston
Keith Carter	Laura McPhee	Edward Weston
Henri Cartier-Bresson	Richard Misrach	Minor White
William Christenberry	Andrea Modica	Marion Post-Wolcott
Linda Connor	Wright Morris	
Imogen Cunningham	Lori Nix	

Walker Evans, *Garage in Southern City Outskirts (Atlanta)*, 1936
Vintage gelatin silver print

Gitterman Gallery

170 East 75th Street
New York, NY 10021

tel: 212-734-0868
fax: 212-734-0869
e-mail: info@gittermangallery.com
web: www.gittermangallery.com

Tom Gitterman
Abigail Feldman
Elena John

Hours: Wednesday - Saturday 11-6
And By Appointment

Gitterman Gallery specializes in the medium of photography. We exhibit and represent artists and estates while also maintaining an inventory of work in a full range of styles and periods.

Erich Angenendt	Robert Frank	William D. Richardson
Roswell Angier	Lee Friedlander	Franz Roh
Eugène Atget	William Garnett	Theodore Roszak
Arthur S. Aubry	William Gedney	Aaron Rothman
Édouard Baldus	Mario Giacomelli	Arthur Rothstein
Machiel Botman	Nan Goldin	Robert Schiller
Pierre Boucher	Ed Grazda	Ernst Schwitters
Constantin Brancusi	Frank Jay Haynes	Aaron Siskind
Bill Brandt	William Henry Jackson	Eduard J. Steichen
Debbie Fleming Caffery	Pierre Jahan	Alfred Stieglitz
Harry Callahan	Michael Kenna	Joseph Szabo
Roger Catherineau	André Kertész	Maurice Tabard
Ken Collins	Francois Kollar	Charles Traub
Eugène Cuvelier	Charles Lindsay	Lloyd Ullberg
Louis De Clercq	Joshua Lutz	James Van Der Zee
Walker Evans	Daniel Masclet	Brett Weston
Gerard Petrus Fieret	Roger Mayne	Edward Weston
Joan Foncuberta	Jean Moral	Minor White
Allen Frame	Roger Parry	Charles Wong

Lindsay McCrum, *Miss Nicole, Age 5*, 2005
Archival pigment print, 52 x 40 inches, edition of 6

Fay Gold Gallery

764 Miami Circle
Atlanta, GA 30324

tel: 404-233-3843
fax: 404-365-8633
e-mail: info@faygoldgallery.com
web: www.faygoldgallery.com

Fay Gold
Amy Miller
Veronica Kessenich

Hours: Tuesday - Saturday 9:30-5:30

Contemporary Photography

Imogen Cunningham	Lindsay McCrum
Andre De Dienes	Arno Minkkinen
Ruth Dusseault	Brian Oglesbee
Rick Ehrlich	Ruth Orkin
William Eggleston	Herb Ritts
Mario Di Girolamo	Sandy Skoglund
Horst P. Horst	Doug & Mike Starn
Bob Kolbrener	Maggie Taylor
David Levinthal	Joyce Tenneson
Robert Mapplethorpe	Jerry Uelsmann
Paolo Mazzanti	

Martin Munkacsi, *Fred Astaire*, 1936
Gelatin silver print, printed c. 1936

Howard Greenberg Gallery

41 East 57th Street, Suite 1406
New York, NY 10022

tel: 212-334-0010
fax: 212-941-7479
e-mail: info@howardgreenberg.com
web: www.howardgreenberg.com

Howard Greenberg
Margit Erb
Karen Marks

Hours: Tuesday - Saturday 10-6

The Gallery specializes in Classic 20th Century Photography with emphasis on photojournalism (FSA, Magnum, Photo League, Civil Rights), New York School, European and American Modernism (1920-1940), Fashion, The Photo Secession (Camerawork), and represents the vintage prints from the Time/LIFE archive.

Berenice Abbott	Mario Giacomelli	Inge Morath
Diane Arbus	Ralph Gibson	Martin Munkacsi
Frédéric Brenner	Allen Ginsberg	Arnold Newman
Esther Bubley	Frank Gohlke	Ruth Orkin
Bill Burke	Phillipe Halsman	Gordon Parks
Robert Capa	Dave Heath	Marc Riboud
Keith Carter	Eikoh Hosoe	Peter Sekaer
Henri Cartier-Bresson	Kenro Izu	Ben Shahn
Simon Chaput	Charles Jones	Aaron Siskind
Ted Croner	André Kertész	W. Eugene Smith
Imogen Cunningham	William Klein	Edward Steichen
Bruce Davidson	Arthur Leipzig	Paul Strand
Mike Disfarmer	Saul Leiter	Josef Sudek
Harold Edgerton	Leon Levinstein	James Van Der Zee
Alfred Eisenstaedt	Rebecca Lepkoff	Roman Vishniac
Walker Evans	George Platt Lynes	Weegee
Louis Faurer	Charles Marville	Dan Weiner
Martine Franck	Sarah Moon	Edward Weston
William Gedney	Charles Moore	Minor White

Doug and Mike Starn, *Blot Out the Sun 2*, 1999-2007

HackelBury Fine Art Limited

4 Launceston Place
London, W8 5RL, England

tel: 44-207-937-8688
fax: 44-207-937-8868
e-mail: gallery@hackelbury.co.uk
web: www.hackelbury.co.uk

Marcus Bury
Sascha Hackel
Kate Stevens

Hours: Tuesday - Saturday 12-5
And By Appointment

Specializing in Fine 20th and 21st Century Photography

Representing	**Works by**
Edward Dimsdale	Berenice Abbott
Elliott Erwitt	Diane Arbus
Martine Franck	Harry Callahan
Frank Horvat	Henri Cartier-Bresson
Stephen Inggs	Ted Croner
Allan Jenkins	Andy Goldsworthy
Michael Kenna	Horst P. Horst
David Michael Kennedy	Seydou Keïta
Pascal Kern	André Kertész
Katia Liebmann	William Klein
Roderick Packe	Arthur Leipzig
Marc Riboud	Linda McCartney
Liz Rideal	Garry Fabian Miller
Malick Sidibé	Richard Misrach
Dennis Stock	Arnold Newman
Phillippe Ughetto	Irving Penn
Masao Yamamoto	Willy Ronis
	Sebastião Salgado
	Victor Schrager
	Cindy Sherman
	Doug & Mike Starn
	Hiroshi Sugimoto
	Steve Szabo
	Alexandre Vitkine

Imogen Cunningham, *Phoenix Recumbent,* 1923
Vintage silver gelatin print

August Sander, *Farmer,* 1923
Vintage gelatin silver print

The Halsted Gallery

PO Box 130
Bloomfield Hills, MI 48303

tel: 248-745-0062
e-mail: info@halstedgallery.com
web: www.halstedgallery.com

Thomas Halsted
Wendy Halsted Beard

Hours: By Appointment

Established in 1969, The Halsted Gallery is dedicated to the education and promotion of fine art photography. The gallery maintains an inventory of 19th and 20th century as well as contemporary photography.

Berenice Abbott
Ansel Adams
Jesse Alexander
Joan Almond
Ruth Bernhard
Bill Brandt
Adolphe Braun
A.M. Bravo
Henri Cartier Bresson
Julia Margaret Cameron
Mark Citret
A. L. Coburn
Imogen Cunningham
Edward S. Curtis
Peter Henry Emerson
Frederick Evans
Walker Evans
Lyle Gomes
Kimberley Gremellion
Hill & Adamson
Lewis Hine
Jack Delano
Don Hong-Oai
William Henry Jackson
Yosuf Karsh
Michael Kenna
André Kertész
Henrich Kuehn

Barbara Macklowe
Barbara Morgan
Leonard Missone
Wright Morris
William Mortensen
Arnold Newman
Irving Penn
Willy Ronis
Arthur Rothstein
August Sander
Bill Schwab
George Seeley
Greg Seman
Aaron Siskind
W. Eugene Smith

Larry Snider
Edward Steichen
Ralph Steiner
Karl Struss
Josef Sudek
George Tice
Jerry Uelsmann
Carleton Watkins
Brett Weston
Cole Weston
Edward Weston
Minor White
Marion Post Wolcott
Steef Zoetmulder
Ion Zupcu

Michael Kenna, *Skyline #1, Hong Kong*, 2006
Geltin silver print

Irving Penn, *Girl in a Manta, Cuzco, Peru*, 1948
Vintage silver print

Charles A. Hartman Fine Art

2625 NE 26th Avenue
Portland, OR 97212

tel: 503-287-3886
e-mail: charles@hartmanfineart.net
web: www.hartmanfineart.net

Charles A. Hartman

Hours: By Appointment

**Specializing in Fine 20th Century
Contemporary and Vintage Photographs**

Ansel Adams
Laure Albin-Guillot
Josef Bartuska
Ruth Bernhard
Ilse Bing
Werner Bischof
Bill Brandt
Harry Callahan
Paul Caponigro
Walter Chappell
William Clift
John Cohen
Carlotta Corpron
Imogen Cunningham
Frantisek Drtikol
Robert Erickson
Walker Evans

Robert Frank
Jaromir Funke
Emmet Gowin
Rosalie Gwathmey
Dave Heath
Lewis Hine
Michael Kenna
André Kertész
Myron Kozman
Danny Lyon
Ralph Eugene Meatyard
Laszlo Moholy-Nagy
Daido Moriyama
Marvin Newman
Nicholas Nixon
Irving Penn
Nancy Rexroth

Rae Russel
Art Sinsabaugh
Aaron Siskind
W. Eugene Smith
Camille Solyagua
Frederick Sommer
Joseph Sterling
Issei Suda
Josef Sudek
Maurice Tabard
Brett Weston
Edward Weston
Minor White
Garry Winogrand
Marion Post Wolcott

Erwin Olaf, *Caroline*, 2006
Lambda print, 36 x 68 inches

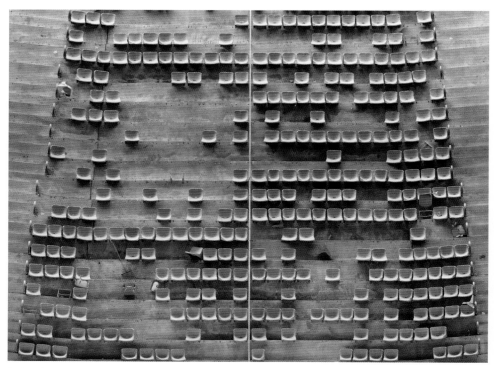

Andreas Gefeller, *Untitled (Stadium), Düsseldorf*, 2002
Digital C-print, 66.9 x 87.4 inches, edition of 8

HASTED HUNT

529 West 20th Street, 3rd floor
New York, NY 10011

tel: 212-627-0006
fax: 212-627-5117
e-mail: info@hastedhunt.com
web: www.hastedhunt.com

Sarah Hasted
W.M. Hunt
Mary-Presely Adams, Director
Zoe Madle, Associate
Lauren Luckett, Registrar

Hours: Tuesday - Saturday 11-6

Hasted Hunt represents outstanding contemporary and vintage photography.

Wilson A. Bentley	Erwin Olaf	**VII**
Lynne Cohen	Eliot Porter	Alexandra Boulat
Michael Flomen	Erich Salomon	Ron Haviv
Andreas Gefeller	Martin Schoeller	Gary Knight
Larry Gianettino	Gerald Slota	Antonin Kratochvil
Jean-Paul Goude	Nicki Stager	Joachim Ladefoged
David Graham	Andrea Stern	Christopher Morris
Bohnchang Koo	Paolo Ventura	James Nachtwey
Luis Mallo	Alex Webb	Eugene Richards
Lisette Model	Joel-Peter Witkin	John Stanmeyer

Martin Schoeller, *Barack Obama*, 2004
Digital C-print, 40 x 50 inches, Edition of 3

Martin Schoeller, *Cate Blanchett*, 2004
Digital C-print, 40 x 50 inches, Edition of 3

Joseph Mills, *Untitled*, 1980s/2002
Varnished gelatin silver print mounted on book cover and found object, 15 x 12 inches

HEMPHILL

1515 14th Street, NW
Washington, DC 20005

tel: 202-234-5601
fax: 202-234-5607
e-mail: gallery@hemphillfinearts.com
web: www.hemphillfinearts.com

George Hemphill
Mary Early
Kimberly Graham
Jessica Lawrence

Hours: Tuesday - Saturday 10-5

HEMPHILL exhibits 20th Century and Contemporary photography. The exhibition schedule features contemporary art across all media.

Corinne May Botz	Don Donaghy	Franz Jantzen
Colby Caldwell	Eliot Elisofon	Tanya Marcuse
William Christenberry	Godfrey Frankel	Joseph Mills
Eduardo del Valle &	Paul Fusco	Portia Munson
Mirta Gomez	Max Hirshfeld	Anne Rowland

William Christenberry, *Green Warehouse, Newbern, Alabama*, 1978
Archival pigment print, 20 x 24 inches

Gustave Le Gray, *Flotte française en rade de Cherbourg*, 1858

Laurent Herschtritt

182 Chemin du Cros
Six Fours Les Plages, 83140, France

tel: 33-6-07-85-63-00
fax: 33-4-94-07-38-76
e-mail: rememberphoto@free.fr
web: www.remember.fr

Laurent Herschtritt

Hours: Offices in Paris, By Appointment Only

Fine 19th and 20th Century Vintage Photographs

Representing
Alexandre Vitkine

No. 73. Amerapoora. Palace of the White Elephant.

The white Elephant is the same Grandloed now in 1826 ; it is now fifty years old ; it has its guards, four white and eight gold Umbrellas, Officers of state, Regalia, &c., &c.

Captain Linnaeus Tripe, *Amerapoora. Palace of the White Elephant*, 1855
Lightly coated salt print from a waxed paper negative, 10 ¹/₂ x 13 ¹/₂ inches

Robert Hershkowitz Ltd.

Cockhaise, Monteswood Lane, Near Lindfield
Sussex, RH16 2QP, England

tel: 44-1444-482-240
fax: 44-1444-484-777
e-mail: prhfoto@hotmail.com

3 Sloane Avenue
London, SW3 3JD, England

tel: 44-20-7581-0362

Robert Hershkowitz, Director
Paula Hershkowitz, Director

Hours: By Appointment

Masterworks of Early European Photography

Hill & Adamson
Eugene Atget
Edouard Baldus
Gustave de Beaucorps
Henri Becquerel
Samuel Bourne
Rev. George Bridges
Julia Margaret Cameron
Lewis Carroll
Desire Charnay
Louis de Clercq
Charles Clifford
W. H. F. Talbot
P. H. Emerson
Frederick Evans
Roger Fenton
F. Fiebig

Andre Giroux
J. B. Greene
Gustave Le Gray
Robert Howlett
Rev. Calvert Jones
R. Macpherson
Charles Marville
L-A Humbert de Molard
Nadar
Charles Negre
Louis Robert
Auguste Salzmann
Henri Le Secq
Felix Teynard
John Thomson
Linnaeus Tripe
Henry White

Imogen Cunningham, *Cactus [Aloe]*, 1925
Vintage silver print

Paul M. Hertzmann, Inc.

PO Box 40447
San Francisco, CA 94140

tel: 415-626-2677
fax: 415-552-4160
e-mail: pmhi@hertzmann.net

Paul Hertzmann, Director
Susan Herzig, Director

Hours: By Appointment

Private dealers since 1974. Specializing in fine vintage nineteenth and twentieth century photographs.

Berenice Abbott
Ansel Adams
Laure Albin-Guillot
Eve Arnold
Eugene Atget
Ruth Bernhard
John Bertolino
Ilse Bing
Erwin Blumenfeld
Margaret Bourke-White
Constantin Brancusi
Bill Brandt
Brassaï
Manuel Alvarez Bravo
Josef Breitenbach
Anne Brigman
Zoe Lowenthal Brown
Francis Bruguiere
Wynn Bullock
Harry Callahan
Henri Cartier-Bresson
Benjamen Chinn
Alvin Langdon Coburn
Imogen Cunningham
William Dassonville
Robert Doisneau
Frantisek Drtikol
Rudolf Eichemeyer
Frederick Evans
Walker Evans
Gerard Fieret
Robert Frank

Jaromir Funke
William Garnett
Arnold Genthe
Mario Giacomelli
Laura Gilpin
Emmet Gowin
Johan Hagemeyer
Pat Harris
Paul Haviland
William Heick
John Hillers
Lewis Hine
Bob Hollingsworth
Lotte Jacobi
Gertrude Kasebier
André Kertész
Heinrich Kuhn
Dorothea Lange
C. Cameron Macauley
Man Ray
Margrethe Mather
Ralph Eugene Meatyard
Tina Modotti
Laszlo Moholy-Nagy
Wright Morris
William Mortensen
Eadweard Muybridge
Arnold Newman
Sonya Noskowiak
Cas Oorthuys
Jose Ortiz-Echague
Timothy O'Sullivan

Paul Outerbridge
Gene Petersen
Nata Piaskowski
F.W. Quandt
Albert Renger Patzsch
Donald Ross
Edward Schwartz
Ben Shahn
Aaron Siskind
Frederick Sommer
Edward Steichen
Alfred Stieglitz
Paul Strand
Karl Struss
Josef Sudek
Doris Ulmann
John Vanderpant
Willard Van Dyke
Pim van Os
Carleton Watkins
Charles Weed
Brett Weston
Edward Weston
Clarence White
Minor White
Marion Post Wolcott
Charles Wong
Max Yavno
Harold Zegart
Steef Zoetmulder
and others

Frederich Seidenstuker, *Untitled, Berlin*, c.1930

Michael Hoppen Gallery Ltd.

3 Jubilee Place
London, SW3 3TD, England

tel: 44-207-352-3649
fax: 44-207-352-3669
e-mail: gallery@michaelhoppengallery.com
web: www.michaelhoppengallery.com

Michael Hoppen
Kathlene Caldwell
Lucy Chadwick

Hours: Tuesday - Friday 12-6, Saturday 10:30-4

Nobuyoshi Araki
Diane Arbus
Richard Avedon
Roger Ballen
Jeff Bark
Lillian Bassman
Peter Beard
Valerie Bélin
Guy Bourdin
Polly Borland
Bill Brandt
Brassaï
Henri Cartier-Bresson
William Claxton
John Davies
Robert Doisneau

Desiree Dolron
Fernand Fonssagrives
Robert Frank
Ken Griffiths
Fergus Greer
Ernst Haas
Hiroshi Hamaya
Lucien Hervé
Scarlett Hooft
E. O. Hoppé
Colin Jones
William Klein
Jacques-Henri Lartigue
Dodo Jin Ming
Sarah Moon
Abelardo Morell

Daido Moriyama
Martin Munkacsi
Matthew Pillsbury
David Parker
Edward Quinn
Giles Revell
Terry Richardson
Frederich Seidenstuker
Joseph Szabo
Hiroshi Sugimoto
Miroslav Tichy
Hiromi Tsuchida
André Villers
Weegee
See our website for
further artists

Brassaï, *Paris*, 1932
Vintage gelatin silver print, 9 x 7 inches

Edwynn Houk Gallery

745 Fifth Avenue
New York, NY 10151

tel: 212-750-7070
fax: 212-688-4848
e-mail: info@houkgallery.com
web: www.houkgallery.com

Edwynn Houk
Julie Castellano
Kirsten Bengtson
John Cowey
Jack Early
Payal Parekh
Erik Rocca

Hours: Tuesday - Saturday 11-6

20th Century Vintage & Contemporary Photography

Diane Arbus
Eugene Atget
The Estate of Ilse Bing
The Estate of Bill Brandt
The Estate of Brassai
Manuel Alvarez Bravo
Margaret Bourke-White
Elinor Carucci
Henri Cartier-Bresson
Imogen Cunningham
Lynn Davis
Elena Dorfman
Elliott Erwitt
Lalla Essaydi

Walker Evans
Sandi Fellman
Robert Frank
Elizabeth Heyert
Andre Kertesz
Germaine Krull
The Estate of Dorothea Lange
Annie Leibovitz
El Lissitzky
Danny Lyon
David Malin
Sally Mann
Joel Meyerowitz
Andrea Modica

Tina Modotti
Laszlo Moholy-Nagy
Paul Outerbridge
Robert Polidori
Man Ray
Alexander Rodchenko
Victor Schrager
Charles Sheeler
Stephen Shore
Alfred Stieglitz
Paul Strand
The Estate of Brett Weston
Edward Weston

Man Ray, *Peggy Guggenheim*, 1924

Jacques-Henri Lartigue, *Zissou caught in the blast of the Amerigo's propeller, Buc, November, 1911*

Hyperion Press Limited

200 West 86th Street
New York, NY 10024

tel: 212-877-2131
fax: 212-769-3907
e-mail: hyperionpr@verizon.net

Monah L. Gettner, Director
Alan Gettner, Co-Director
Dawn Luebbe, Assistant Director

Hours: By Appointment

20th Century Vintage and Contemporary Photographs. Limited Edition Photographs

Man Ray
Eugene Atget
Dieter Appelt
Lewis Baltz
Tom Baril
Hans Bellmer
Edouard Boubat
Bill Brandt
Bragaglia Brothers
Manuel Alvarez Bravo
Louise Dahl-Wolfe
Robert Doisneau
Jacques Dubois
Louis Faurer
Trude Fleischmann
Robert Frank

Ralph Gibson
Horst P. Horst
George Hoyningen-Huene
Frank Horvat
René-Jacques
Andre Kertesz
William Klein
Jacques-Henri Lartigue
Jan Lukas
Danny Lyon
Willy Ronis
Jaroslav Rössler
Edward Steichen
Maurice Tabard
Garry Winogrand

Exclusive Representative For
Jacques-Henri Lartigue

Special Interests
French 20th Century
Photography
Czech Photography

Julia Margaret Cameron, *Stella,* 1867
Albumen print, 11.25 x 9 inches

Charles Isaacs
Photographs, Inc.

25 West 54th Street, #5C
New York, NY 10019

tel: 212-957-3238
e-mail: cti@charlesisaacs.com
web: www.charlesisaacs.com

Charles Isaacs
Carol Nigro

Hours: By Appointment

Since 1980, we have specialized in vintage work of the early 19th and 20th century. We also represent a select group of contemporary artists.

Eugene Atget	Gerard Fieret	Laszlo Moholy-Nagy
Charles Aubry	W. H. Fox Talbot	NASA
Edouard Baldus	Francis Frith	Charles Negre
Bill Brandt	Giraudon's Artist	Timothy O'Sullivan
Dennis Callwood	Hill and Adamson	Louis Robert
Julia Margaret Cameron	William H. Jackson	Auguste Salzmann
Lewis Carroll	Gertrude Kasebier	Carolee Schneemann
Desire Charnay	Andre Kertesz	Jem Southam
Frank Chauvassaignes	William Larson	Linnaeus Tripe
Civil War	Heather Lin	Carleton Watkins
Imogen Cunningham	Gustave Le Gray	Edward Weston
Roger Fenton	Charles Marville	Important Daguerreotypes

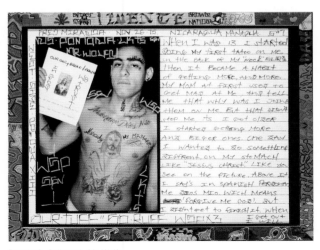

Dennis O. Callwood, *Mr. Wolfy*
C-print in unique graffiti frame, 30 by 40 inches

Mona Kuhn, *Skip a Beat*, 2005

Angela West, *Dad with Machete*, 2005

Jackson Fine Art

3115 East Shadowlawn Avenue
Atlanta, GA 30305

tel: 404-233-3739
fax: 404-233-1205
e-mail: malia@jacksonfineart.com
web: www.jacksonfineart.com

Anna Walker Skillman, Owner
Malia Stewart, Director
Morgan Beasley
Stephanie Dowda, Administrator
Stevie Brown

Hours: Tuesday - Saturday 10-5

20th Century and Contemporary Photography

Anderson & Low
Roger Ballen
Harry Callahan
Henri Cartier-Bresson
Orain E. Catledge
William Christenberry
Mitch Epstein
Elliott Erwitt
F.S.A.
David Fokos
Lynn Geesaman
David Hilliard
Horst P. Horst
Frank Horvat
Birney Imes

Michael Kenna
Andre Kertesz
Mona Kuhn
Annie Leibovitz
Arthur Leipzig
Herman Leonard
Helen Levitt
Sally Mann
Mary Ellen Mark
Raymond Meeks
Ray Metzker
Andrew Moore
Luis Gonzalez Palma
Scott Peterman
Matthew Pillsbury

Richard Renaldi
Willy Ronis
Rocky Schenck
Julius Shulman
Mike Smith
Jack Spencer
Mark Steinmetz
Ron Van Dongen
Ruud van Empel
Eric Weeks
Angela West
Terri Weifenbach
Masao Yamamoto

Jean Geiser, *Woman holding roses in harem setting, artist's study*, c.1870s

Ken & Jenny Jacobson

Southcotts Petches Bridge
Great Bardfield, Essex
CM7 4QN, England

tel: 441-371-810-566
fax: 441-371-810-845
e-mail: ken@jacobsonphoto.com
web: www.jacobsonphoto.com

Ken Jacobson, Director
Jenny Jacobson, Director

Hours: By Appointment

19th Century Photographs

Our 26th consecutive year exhibiting at The Photography Show coincides with the release of a new book by Ken Jacobson: *Odalisques & Arabesques: Orientalist Photography 1839-1925*.

This book, published by Bernard Quaritch, represents the most comprehensive survey to date of 19th and early 20th century photography of both North Africa and the Middle East. Using Orientalist painting as a counterpoint, the work primarily relates the incredibly rich and beautiful history of visual documentation expressed in the photography of the people, daily life and culture of the Orient. There are more than 90 biographies and over 500 illustrations including 85 fine tritone plates as well as unprecedented identification aids that allow the correct attribution of photographers' work that may have hitherto been anonymous or misidentified.

Thomas Annan	Roger Fenton	James Robertson
Felice Beato	Jean Geiser	Henry Peach Robinson
E. Bechard	Giraudon's Artist	Auguste Salzmann
Bisson Freres	Frank Mason Good	Charles Scowen
Felix Bonfils	Herman Heid	Pascal Sebah
Samuel Bourne	W. Hammerschmidt	William Louis Henry Skeen
Adolphe Braun	Rudolf Carl Huber	Giorgio Sommer
A. Brignoli	Kusakabe Kimbei	F.M. Sutcliffe
G.E. Chauffourier	Isodore von Kinsbergen	William H. Pigou
Lala Deen Dayal	August Kotzsch	Baron von Stillfried
Maxime Du Camp	Robert Macpherson	John Thomson
Louis-Émile Durandelle	F.J.-A. Moulin	Pierre Tremaux
P.H. Emerson	Colin Murray	John Claude White
Frederick Fiebig	Herbert Ponting	Woodbury & Page

Stephen Shames, *Huey P. Newton Listens to Bob Dylan's Highway 61 Revisited*, 1970
Vintage gelatin silver print, 10 x 8 inches

Steven Kasher Gallery

521 West 23rd Street, 2nd Floor
New York, NY 10011

tel: 212-966-3978
fax: 212-226-1485
e-mail: info@stevenkasher.com
web: www.stevenkasher.com

Steven Kasher
Gary Owen
Maria Stenina

Hours: Tuesday - Saturday 11-6

19th, 20th, and 21st Century Photography

Henry Clay Anderson	Philip Jones Griffiths	Mugshots
Richard Avedon	Hiroshi Hamaya	Wingate Paine
Bruno Barbey	Matt Herron	Irving Penn
Ian Berry	Lewis Hine	Gilles Peress
Werner Bischof	Dennis Hopper	Lou Reed
Cornell Capa	James Karales	Ira Richer
Robert Capa	Richard Kalvar	Herb Ritts
Civil Rights Movement	Hiroji Kubota	Alexander Rodchenko
William Claxton	Norman Kulkin	George Rodger
D. James Dee	Louise Lawler	Stephen Shames
Raymond Depardon	Erna Lendvai-Dircksen	Marilyn Silverstone
Mike Disfarmer	Danny Lyon	Beuford Smith
Michelle Elzay	Constantine Manos	Dennis Stock
Nathan Farb	Fred W. McDarrah	Allan Tannenbaum
Bob Fitch	Albert Maysles	Tintypes
Leonard Freed	Jeff Mermelstein	James Van der Zee
Burt Glinn	Charles Moore	Monsieur X

John Humble, *View South from Recreation Road, Carson, May 2, 1980*

John Humble, *343 Hillcrest Street, El Segundo, May 13, 1995*

Jan Kesner Gallery

164 North La Brea Avenue
Los Angeles, CA 90036-2912

tel: 323-938-6834
fax: 323-938-1106
e-mail: jankesner@jankesnergallery.com
web: www.jankesnergallery.com

Jan Kesner
Justen Deal

Hours: By Appointment

**Specialists in 20th Century Master
& Contemporary Photography**

The Jan Kesner Gallery is known for a high standard of integrity, taste, and commitment to offering the best works of art by the most important photographers. The Gallery maintains an extensive inventory of artistically and historically significant vintage photographs and also works closely with a highly select group of contemporary artists.

Ansel Adams
Diane Arbus
Eugene Atget
Donald Blumberg
Anne Brigman
Manuel Alvarez Bravo
Nancy Burson
Harry Callahan
Larry Clark
Imogen Cunningham
Walker Evans

Louis Faurer
Tapp Francke
Lewis Hine
Robert Frank
John Humble
Robert Mapplethorpe
Roger Minick
Richard Misrach
Tina Modotti
Frank van der Salm
Jan Saudek

Arne Svenson
Rubén Ortíz Torres
Adriene Veninger
Randy West
Brett Weston
Edward Weston
Garry Winogrand
Dan Winters
Max Yavno
Kim Zwarts

A Place in the Sun: Photographs of Los Angeles by John Humble
at the J. Paul Getty Museum through July 8, 2007
Signed copies of the exhibition publication are available.
jankesnergallery.com/getty

Richard Pare (*1948), *The Lenin Mausoleum, Moscow. Alexei Schusev, 1924-30*, 1998
Digital laser print, ca. 122 x 152 centimeters, Edition of 5

Kicken Berlin

Linienstrasse 155 / 161a
Berlin, 10115, Germany

tel: 49-30-288-77-88-2
fax: 49-30-288-77-88-3
e-mail: kicken@kicken-gallery.com
web: www.kicken-gallery.com

Annette Kicken
Rudolf Kicken

Hours: Tuesday - Saturday 2-6

Since 1974 Kicken Berlin has specialized in 19th- and 20th-century and contemporary photography. Since its foundation the gallery has explored the relationship between photography and the other arts in over 220 exhibitions. It maintains a large collection of high quality master-prints from 1900 to 1950.

Dieter Appelt
Bauhaus
Bernd & Hilla Becher
Karl Blossfeldt
Anna & Bernhard Blume
Goetz Diergarten
Ed van der Elsken
fotoform
Janos Frecot
Charles Fréger
Lee Friedlander
F.C. Gundlach
Jitka Hanzlová
Rudolf Koppitz
Helmar Lerski

Werner Mantz
Ryuji Miyamoto
Péter Nádas
Arnold Newman
Helmut Newton
Richard Pare
Albert Renger-Patzsch
Heinrich Riebesehl
Hans-Christian Schink
Wilhelm Schürmann
Alfred Seiland
Stephen Shore
Otto Steinert
Christer Strömholm
Umbo (Otto Umbehr)

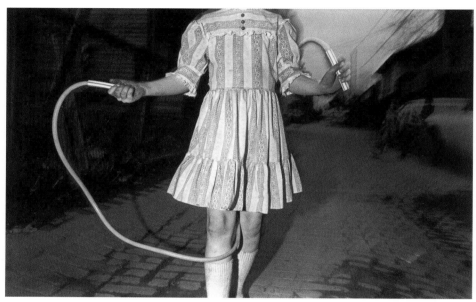

Mark Cohen, *jump rope,* 1975

BOOTH #100

Robert Klein Gallery

38 Newbury Street, 4th Floor
Boston, MA 02116

tel: 617-267-7997
fax: 617-267-5567
e-mail: inquiry@robertkleingallery.com
web: www.robertkleingallery.com

Robert Klein
Eunice Hurd
Drea Plummer
Jessica Turner

Hours: Tuesday - Friday 10-5:30
Saturday 11-5

Classic and Contemporary Photographs

19th Century
Edouard-Denis Baldus
Antonio Beato
Louis De Clercq
Edward S. Curtis
Julia Margaret Cameron
J.B. Greene
Eadweard Muybridge
Charles Negre
William Henry Fox Talbot
Carleton E. Watkins

20th Century
Berenice Abbott
Ansel Adams
Diane Arbus
Eugène Atget
Brassaï
Harry Callahan
Henri Cartier-Bresson
Mark Cohen
Elliott Erwitt
Walker Evans
Mario Giacomelli
Lewis Hine
Horst P. Horst
Yousuf Karsh

André Kertész
William Klein
Jacques-Henri Lartigue
Helen Levitt
O. Winston Link
Irving Penn
Aaron Siskind
Ralph Steiner
Jerry Uelsmann
Brett Weston
Edward Weston

Contemporary
Jesse Alexander
Roger Ballen
Tom Baril
Alvin Booth
Jeff Brouws
Carl Chiarenza
Stephen DiRado
Elena Dorfman
John Dugdale
Beth Yarnelle Edwards
David Fokos
Sally Gall
Lajos Geenen
Carol Golemboski

Chip Hooper
Paul Ickovic
Bill Jacobson
Michael Kenna
Laura Letinsky
Michael Light
Chema Madoz
Didier Massard
D.W. Mellor
Arno Rafael Minkkinen
Luis Gonzalez Palma
Olivia Parker
Herb Ritts
Michal Ronnen Safdie
Sebastião Salgado
Tomio Seike
Rodney Smith
Jock Sturges
Hiroshi Sugimoto
George Tice
Tseng Kwong Chi
Adriene Veninger
William Wegman
Terri Weifenbach
Wang Wusheng
Masao Yamamoto
Anne Zahalka

Shi Guorui, *Shanghai*

Alan Klotz Gallery

511 West 25th Street, Suite 701
New York, NY 10001

tel: 212-741-4764
fax: 212-741-4760
e-mail: info@klotzgallery.com
web: www.klotzgallery.com

Alan Klotz, Director
Peter C. Emerick, Gallery Manager

Hours: Wednesday - Saturday 12-6

Celebrating our 30th Year!

19th Century	**20th Century**	LIFE
Fratelli Alinari	Berenice Abbott	Eliot Porter
Edouard-Denis Baldus	Ansel Adams	Edward Quigley
Felice Beato	Eugene Atget	Arthur Rothstein
Bisson-Freres	Brassaï	Aaron Siskind
Felix Bonfils	Margaret Bourke-White	W. Eugene Smith
Samuel Bourne	Harry Callahan	Alfred Stieglitz
Adolphe Braun	Camera Work	Josef Sudek
Julia Margaret Cameron	Carlotta Corpron	Edward Weston
China	Edward S. Curtis	Minor White
Louis DeClercq	Czech Photography	
Louis-Emile Durandelle	Frantisek Drtikol	**Contemporary**
Peter Henry Emerson	Alfred Eisenstaedt	Pavel Banka
Francis Frith	Walker Evans	Rebecca Cummins
India	Andreas Feininger	Alyson Denny
Italy	Robert Frank	Alex Emmons
William H.Jackson	F.S.A	Gilbert Fastenaekens
Japan	Jaromir Funke	Alida Fish
Robert MacPherson	Mario Giacomelli	Terri Garland
Charles Marville	Lewis Hine	Shi Guorui
Middle East	Gertrude Kasebier	Robert Levin
Eadweard Muybridge	André Kertész	Corinne Mercadier
Nadar	Imre Kinszki	Philip Perkis
Timothy O'Sullivan	Dorothea Lange	Melissa Ann Pinney
August Salzmann	Harry Lapow	Robert Richfield
William H.F. Talbot	Russel Lee	Jonathan Torgovnik
Felix Teynard		
Carleton Watkins		

Michael Wolf, *Copy Art #42, Gerhard Richter $32*, 2006
Chromogenic print

Edward Burtynsky, *Iberian Quarries #2, Bencatel, Portugal*, 2006
Chromogenic print

Robert Koch Gallery

49 Geary Street, 5th Floor
San Francisco, CA 94108

tel: 415-421-0122
fax: 415-421-6306
e-mail: info@kochgallery.com
web: www.kochgallery.com

Robert Koch
Ada Takahashi

Hours: Tuesday - Saturday 10:30-5:30

19th, 20th Century and Contemporary Photography

19th Century
Edouard Baldus
Felice Beato
Julia Margaret Cameron
Lewis Carroll
Francis Frith
John B. Greene
John Hillers
Gustave Le Gray
Henri Le Secq
Charles Marville
Eadweard Muybridge
Timothy O'Sullivan
W. H. Fox Talbot
Linnaeus Tripe
Carleton Watkins

20th Century
Ansel Adams
Eugène Atget
Bill Brandt
Brassaï
Henri Cartier-Bresson
Imogen Cunningham
Edward S. Curtis
Frantisek Drtikol
Dr. Harold Edgerton
Robert Frank
Jaromír Funke
Mario Giacomelli
Florence Henri
Boris Ignatovich
Yousuf Karsh
Gyorgy Kepes
André Kertész
Yevgeny Khaldei
Imre Kinszki
Dora Maar
Man Ray
László Moholy-Nagy
Irving Penn
Alexander Rodchenko
Jaroslav Rossler
Josef Sudek
Brett Weston
Edward Weston
Clarence White
Georgy Zelma

Contemporary
Tom Baril
Debra Bloomfield
Jeff Brouws
Edward Burtynsky
Debbie Fleming Caffery
Carl De Keyzer
Elliott Erwitt
Lynn Geesaman
Lauren Greenfield
Simen Johan
Josef Koudelka
Wayne Levin
Sally Mann
Duane Michals
Mario Cravo Neto
Bill Owens
David Parker
Christian Patterson
Jan Saudek
Larry Schwarm
Mike Smith
Jock Sturges
Brian Ulrich
Jo Whaley
Michael Wolf
and others

Collections
Czech
Hungarian
Russian

Thomas Wrede, *Haus auf Hochebene*

Paul Kopeikin Gallery

6150 Wilshire Boulevard
Los Angeles, CA 90048

tel: 323-937-0765
fax: 323-937-5974
e-mail: info@paulkopeikingallery.com
web: www.paulkopeikingallery.com

Paul Kopeikin
Kaycee Olsen

Hours: Tuesday - Saturday 11-6
And By Appointment

Contemporary Art and Photography

J. Bennett Fitts
Stern J. Bramson Estate
Chan Chao
Rick Chapman
Seth Dickerman
David DiMichele
Steve Fitch
David Fokos
Jona Frank
Amanda Friedman
David Graham
Henry Horenstein
Chris Jordan
Nicholas Kahn &
   Richard Selesnick
Mark Klett
Ethan Levitas
Helen Levitt
Robert Lyons
David Maisel
Jeffrey Milstein
Rachel Papo
Angelika Rinnhofer
Lisa Robinson
Lukas Roth
Lynn Saville
Amy Stein
Karl Struss Estate
Garry Winogrand
Marion Post Wolcott
Thomas Wrede
Jody Zellen

Chris Jordan, *Denali Denial*

Joseph, vicomte Vigier, *Landscape at Pau taken from the Pyrénées,* 1853
Salt print from a paper negative, 24.2 x 33.2 cm

Hans P. Kraus, Jr. Inc.

962 Park Avenue at 82nd Street
New York, NY 10028

tel: 212-794-2064
fax: 212-744-2770
e-mail: info@sunpictures.com

Hans P. Kraus, Jr.
Jennifer Parkinson
Russell Lord
Shelley Dowell

Hours: By Appointment

BOOTH #401

**Old Masters of Photography
Since 1984**

Aguado	Fenton	Negre
Anna Atkins	Fizeau	Regnault
Atget	J.B. Greene	Rejlander
Aubry	Henneman	Robert
Baldus	Hill & Adamson	Ross
Bayard	Calvert Jones	Salzmann
Bisson Freres	Le Dien & Le Gray	Southworth & Hawes
Mrs. Cameron	Le Gray	Steichen
Caneva	Le Secq	Story-Maskelyne
Carroll	Llewelyn	Talbot
Coburn	MacPherson	Teynard
Cuvelier	Marey	Capt. Tripe
De Clercq	Marville	B.B. Turner
F.H. Evans	Murray	Vigier
Fardon	Nadar	And others

Announcing: Sun Pictures Catalogue XVI
Joseph, vicomte Vigier, *Voyage dans les Pyrénées,* 1853

Joel Peter Witkin, *The Raft of G.W. Bush*, 2006
74.5 x 89 centimeters, Edition of 15

Clark & Pougnaud, *Caroline*, 2005
Lambda print, 50 X 60 centimeters, Edition of 9

baudoin lebon

38, rue Sainte Croix de la Bretonnerie
Paris, 75004, France

tel: 33-1-42-72-09-10
fax: 33-1-42-72-02-20
e-mail: baudoin.lebon@wanadoo.fr
web: www.baudoin-lebon.com

Baudoin Lebon
Anne Le Tri
Caroline Bouchard

Hours: Tuesday - Saturday 11-7

19th, 20th Century and Contemporary Photographs

Estates
Lisette Model
Harry H. Lunn
Texbraun
Jeanloup Sieff

Artists
Patrick Bailly-Maitre-Grand
Mathieu Bernard-Reymond
Song Chao
Clark & Pougnaud
Christian Courreges
Bertrand Desprez
Carole Fekete
Caroline Feyt
Henri Foucault
Gladys

Harald Gottschalk
Mimmo Jodice
Les Krims
Dany Leriche
Chrystele Lerisse
Didier Massard
Byung-Hun Min
Yuji Ono
Olivier Rebufa
Michel Szulc-Krzyzanowski
Joel Peter Witkin

Louis Alphonse de Brebisson, *La croix de Grisy,
près de Falaise*, c. 1853
Salt paper, 22 x 17 centimeters

Rex Dupain (b. 1954), *Splash Man*, 2006
C-type photograph

Matthew Sleeth (b. 1972), *Untitled #5 [Tokyo]*, 2002
C-type photograph

Josef Lebovic Gallery

34 Paddington Street (PO Box 453)
Paddington, NSW 2021
Sydney, Australia

tel: 61-2-9332-1840
fax: 61-2-9331-7431
e-mail: josef@joseflebovicgallery.com
web: www.joseflebovicgallery.com

Josef Lebovic
Jeanne M. Lebovic

Hours: Wednesday - Friday 1-6, Saturday 11-5

Australian & International Original Works on Paper & Photographs. Established 1977

19th, 20th Century and Contemporary Australian Photography

Greg Barrett	Fiona Hall	Henri Mallard
Robert Besanko	Bill Henson	David Moore Estate
Cecil Bostock	Brett Hilder	Charles Page
Anthony Browell	Rob Hillier	Tim Page
William G. Buckle	Ruth Hollick	Axel Poignant
Nicholas Caire	Frank Hurley	David Potts
Jack Cato	John Kauffmann	Philip Quirk
Harold Cazneaux	Charles Kerry	Roger Scott
Olive Cotton Estate	Henry King	Wolfgang Sievers
Raymond De Berquelle	Laurence Le Guay	Matthew Sleeth
Kerry Dundas	Jon Lewis	Heide Smith
Max Dupain	J.W. Lindt	Robin Smith
Rex Dupain	Monte Luke	Elaine Pelot Syron
John B. Eaton	Graham McCarter	Mark Tedeschi
Freeman Bros	Robert McFarlane	Greg Weight
Juno Gemes	Sally McInerney	Robert Whitaker

Frank Hurley (1885-1962),
*Royal Penguins on Nugget's Beach,
Macquarie Island*, 1911
Silver gelatin photograph

Max Dupain (1911-1992),
Sunbaker, 1937 / later printing
Silver gelatin photograph

Dorothea Lange, *Demonstration, San Francisco,* 1933
Gelatin silver print, 9 ³/₄ x 7 ¹/₂

Lee Gallery

Nine Mount Vernon Street, 2nd Floor
Winchester, MA 01890

tel: 781-729-7445
fax: 781-729-4592
e-mail: apd@leegallery.com
web: www.leegallery.com

Mack Lee
Michael Lee
Erica Lee

Hours: Monday - Friday 10-5
And By Appointment

Fine 19th and 20th Century Photographs

Berenice Abbott	Roger Fenton	Sonya Noskowiak
Eugene Atget	Leonard Freed	Auguste Salzmann
Edouard Baldus	Francis Frith	George H. Seeley
George Barnard	Alexander Gardner	W. Eugene Smith
Ilse Bing	Samuel Gottscho	Edward Steichen
Bisson Freres	Paul Haviland	Alfred Stieglitz
Margaret Bourke-White	David Octavius Hill	Paul Strand
Bill Brandt	Robert Adamson	Karl Struss
Adolphe Braun	Lewis Hine	Frank Meadow Sutcliffe
Annie Brigman	Gertrude Kasebier	Linnaeus Tripe
Alvin Langdon Coburn	Heinrich Kuhn	Carleton Watkins
Eugene Cuvelier	Dorothea Lange	Todd Webb
William Dassonville	Edwin Hale Lincoln	Weegee
Robert Demachy	Charles Marville	Brett Weston
Maxime Du Camp	Wayne Miller	Edward Weston
Peter Henry Emerson	Wright Morris	Clarence White
Frederick H. Evans	Eadweard Muybridge	Camera Work
Walker Evans	Charles Negre	Others

Horation Ross, 1858
Waxed paper negative, 11 x 13.75 inches

Janet Lehr, Inc.

891 Park Avenue
New York, NY 10021

tel: 212-288-1802
fax: 212-288-6234
e-mail: janetlehr@janetlehrinc.com
web: www.janetlehrinc.com

Weekends and Summers
Vered Gallery, 68 Park Place
East Hampton, NY 11937

tel/fax: 631-324-3303

Janet Lehr
Nicolas Hoyos
Damien Roman
Vered

Hours: By Appointment

Specialists in both 19th and 20th Century Master Photographs and Collection Development

Classic
Eugene Atget
*Edouard-Denis Baldus
Matthew Brady
*Adolphe Braun
*Julia Margaret Cameron
*Alvin Langdon Coburn
*Edward Sherif Curtis
Louis De Clercq
*Thomas Eakins
Frederick Evans
*Walker Evans
*Roger Fenton
*Francis Frith
Alexander Gardner
*John Beasley Greene
D.o.Hill and Robert Adamson
*Jack Hillers
*William Henry Jackson
Reverend Calvert Jones

Dorothea Lange
Gustave Le Gray
*Man Ray
Edweard Muybridge
Nadar (Gaspard Felix
Tournachon)
Charles Negre
Timothy O'Sullivan
*Robert Redfield
Oscar Gustave Rejlander
Louis Roberts
Henry Peach Robinson
*Horatio Ross
*Arthur Rothstein
*Andrew Joseph Russell
Auguste Salzmann
*Ben Shahn
Edward Steichen
Alfred Stieglitz
Albert Southworth and Joshia

Hawes
William Henry Fox Talbot
*John Thomson
Linneasus Tripe
Vallou Villeneuve
*Carleton E Watkins
Edward Weston
Clarence White
*Minor White
*Louise Deshong Woodbridge

Contemporary
Nan Golden
Steven Klein
Vic Muniz
Helmut Newton
Cindy Sherman
Bert Stern

Asterisk denotes collections

Bernhard Fuchs, *Roter Ford-Bus, bei Freistadt (A)*, 1994
Chromogenic print, 16 x 20 inches

gallery luisotti

2525 Michigan Avenue, #A-2
Santa Monica, CA 90404

tel: 310-453-0043
fax: 310-264-4888
e-mail: info@galleryluisotti.com
web: artnet.com/luisotti.html

Theresa Luisotti
Alex Weber
Emily Hara

Hours: Tuesday - Friday 10:30-6
Saturday 11-6

A special emphasis on the 1970s New Topographics movement, and a focus on mid-career and emerging photographers working within this tradition.

Lewis Baltz
Frank Breuer
Joachim Brohm
Terry Evans
Christina Fernandez
Bernhard Fuchs
Shirley Irons
Barbara Kasten
Jacques Henri Lartigue
Lewis Morley

Simone Nieweg
Simon Norfolk
Heinrich Riebesehl
Milton Rogovin
Tata Ronkholz
Mark Ruwedel
Wilhelm Schürmann
Toshio Shibata
Catherine Wagner
Henry Wessel

Works By
Imogen Cunningham
Walker Evans
Mike Mandel
Michael C. McMillen
Lisette Model
August Sander
Oreste Selvatico

Felix Teynard, *Karnak (Thebes)*
Salt print 1853-54, from a paper negative 1851-52
11 $^9/_{16}$ x 5 $^7/_{16}$ inches

Ezra Mack

Services Provided Everywhere

Mailing Address:
PO Box 5090
Greenwich, CT 06831

tel: 310-863-3467
e-mail: fineartcom@aol.com

Hours: By appointment

Vintage Masterworks and experiments are available by the following artists; individual works and collections bought and sold. Inquiries welcomed.

19th Century
Anna Atkins
Edouard Baldus
Camille Corot
Eugene Cuvelier
Peter Henry Emerson
Hippolyte Fizeau
Francis Frith
J. B. Greene
Nicholaas Henneman
Hill & Adamson
Rev. Calvert R Jones
Gustave LeGray

Jean-Francois Millet
Charles Negre
August Salzman
William Henry Fox Talbot
Linneaus Tripe
Vallou de Villeneuve
Carleton Watkins

20th Century
Ansel Adams
Constantin Brancusi
Christo
Alvin Langdon Coburn

F. Holland Day
F. H. Evans
Robert Mapplethorpe
Henry Moore
Paul Outerbridge, Jr.
Edward Steichen
Paul Strand
Edward Weston
Joel-Peter Witkin

Important Daguerreotypes,
Ambrotypes, and Tin Types
and others

Bruno Braquehais, *Nu Féminin à la Coiffure de Perles, c.1858-1860*
Colored Stereo Daguerreotype, 2 $\frac{1}{2}$ x 6 $\frac{1}{4}$ inches

Chip Hooper, *Cape Foulwind Beach, Tasman Sea*, 2003
From the upcoming exhibition 'Chip Hooper: New Zealand's South Pacific & Tasman Sea' (March 29 - May 12, 2007)

Robert Mann Gallery

210 Eleventh Avenue, 10th Floor
New York, NY 10001

tel: 212-989-7600
fax: 212-989-2947
e-mail: mail@robertmann.com
web: www.robertmann.com

Robert Mann
Caroline Cohen
Devin Grosz

Hours: Tuesday - Saturday 11-6

20th and 21st Century Photographs
and Photo-Based Mixed Media

Berenice Abbott	Stephen Hughes	ringl+pit
Ansel Adams	Michael Kenna	Leo Rubinfien
Gail Albert Halaban	O. Winston Link	Aaron Siskind
Diane Arbus	Mary Mattingly	W. Eugene Smith
Ellen Auerbach	Maria Miesenberger	Jem Southam
Jeff Brouws	Laurent Millet	Alfred Stieglitz
Joe Deal	Richard Misrach	Paul Strand
Wijnanda Deroo	Lisette Model	David Vestal
Walker Evans	Artur Nikodem	Margaret Watkins
Robbert Flick	Luis Gonzalez Palma	Weegee
Masahisa Fukase	Charles Pratt	Dan Weiner
Leslie Gill	Susan Rankaitis	Henry Wessel
Elijah Gowin	Man Ray	Minor White
Grzeszykowska & Smaga	res	Silvio Wolf
Chip Hooper	Nancy Rexroth	

Jen Davis, *Untitled 21*, 2005
Chromogenic color photograph, 24 x 20 inches, edition of 10, 14 x 11 inches, edition of 15

Lee Marks Fine Art

2208 East 350 North
Shelbyville, IN 46176

tel: 317-398-9212
fax: 317-398-2242
e-mail: lee@leemarksfineart.com
web: www.leemarksfineart.com

Lee Marks
John C. DePrez, Jr.

Hours: By Appointment

19th, 20th Century & Contemporary Photography

Berenice Abbott	Mariana Cook	Eadweard Muybridge
Diane Arbus	Jen Davis	Irving Penn
Eugene Atget	Lucinda Devlin	Brad Richman
Morley Baer	Frederick Evans	Neil Selkirk
Jeffrey Becom	Walker Evans	Art Sinsabaugh
Karl Blossfeldt	Robert Frank	Mike Smith
Andrew Borowiec	Lee Friedlander	W. Eugene Smith
Wendy Burton	Linda Adele Goodine	Peter Turnley
Caithness & Bembridge	Lewis Hine	Adam Clark Vroman
Harry Callahan	Hiro	Garry Winogrand
Camera Work Gravures	Dora Maar	Wols
Robert Capa	Tyagan Miller	And others

Laurence Aberhart, *Dimboola, Victoria, 13 August, 1997*
Silver gelatin gold & selenium toned contact print, 8 x 10 inches

McNamara Gallery Photography

190 Wicksteed Street
Wanganui, 4500, New Zealand

tel: 64-6-348-7320
e-mail: mcnamaraphotogal@xtra.co.nz
web: www.mcnamara.co.nz

Paul McNamara

Hours: Wednesday - Saturday 11-3
And By Appointment

McNamara Gallery Photography opened 25.1.02 and exhibits New Zealand, & selected Pacific Rim, photographically-based art. We are dedicated to exhibiting and promoting the medium, and exploring the range of practice.

Our interest is fundamentally in modern & contemporary art practice; however, we have an annual exhibition examining photographs from the 1960s -1980s. We also exhibit selected work from earlier periods.

We have monthly exhibitions and represent a large number of N.Z. and some international artists. We also produce out-reach exhibitions.

Aberhart Laurence	Crowley Lisa	Orjis Richard
Adams Mark	Daley John S.	Pardington Fiona
Amundsen Fiona	Fritchley Hayden	Pardington Neil
Barrar Wayne	Glass Darren	Peryer Peter
Bayly Janet	Hamon Neil [UK]	Robertson Natalie
Beran Grant	Hartigan Paul	Rotman Jono
Black Peter	Henderson Derek [Australia/UK]	Sameshima Haruhika
Blackman Gary	Johns John[Estate]	Shelton Ann
Bosworth Rhondda	Johns Paul	Smith Ross T.
Campaner Elaine [Australia]	Knowles Alan	Tocher Hamish
Campbell Joyce	Kokx Nikolai	Van Royen, David [Australia]
Cammick Murray	Macdolald Ian	Webster, Christine
Cauchi Ben	Neate Robin	Wesney, Len
Clark Fiona	Noble Anne	Westra, Ans
Collins Richard	Nola Tanja	Wilson - Wong Wayne
Connew Bruce	Oettli Max	Zusters Jane

Narelle Autio, *Untitled, from the series, The Seventh Wave*, 1999/2000
31.5 x 47 inches, Edition of 15

Ariel Meyerowitz

4720 Center Blvd., Suite 2005
Long Island City, NY 11109

tel: 212-414-2770
fax: 212-961-0505
e-mail: ariel@arielmeyerowitz.com
web: www.arielmeyerowitz.com

Ariel Meyerowitz

Hours: By Appointment

Ariel Meyerowitz, Private Dealer and Art Advisor, specializes in 20th Century vintage and contemporary photography, painting and works-on-paper. In addition to representing select photographers and estates, the focus of her art consultancy is to advise private and corporate clients on acquiring new works, managing collections and/or building upon existing collections. Advising both sophisticated buyers and novice collectors alike, Ariel works across all media. Ariel has worked in the art community for 15 years and until 2006 had owned her eponymous photography gallery for 6 years.

Narelle Autio
Tom Blake
Richard Caldicott
Don James
Chad Kleitsch
Joel Meyerowitz
Trent Parke
George Tice

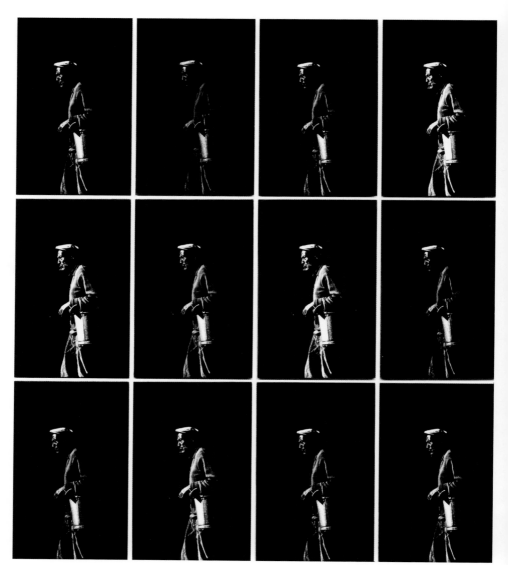

Ray K. Metzker, *Who-bee*, 1966-2006

Laurence Miller Gallery

20 West 57th Street
New York, NY 10019

tel: 212-397-3930
fax: 212-397-3932
e-mail: contact@laurencemillergallery.com
web: www.laurencemillergallery.com

Laurence Miller, President
Vicki Harris, Director
Mark Mann, Associate Director
Jody Berman, Assistant Director

Hours: Tuesday - Friday 10-5:30
Saturday 11-5:30

Diane Arbus
Zeke Berman
Peter Bialobrzeski
Larry Burrows
Joan Colom
Stephane Couturier
Duane Hanson
Fan Ho
Yasuhiro Ishimoto
Helen Levitt
Julie Mack
Mark Mann

Ray Metzker
DoDo Jin Ming
Edweard Muybridge
David Plowden
Toshio Shibata
Kenneth Snelson
Michael Spano
Maggie Taylor
Val Telberg
Ruth Thorne-Thomsen
Jerry Uelsmann
Burk Uzzle

Bill Henson, *Untitled 2005/06*, 2005-06
Type "C" color photograph, 50 x 70 ⅞ inches, 127 x 180.02 centimeters, Edition of 5
© Bill Henson, Courtesy Robert Miller Gallery, New York

Robert Miller Gallery

524 West 26th Street
New York, NY 10001

tel: 212-366-4774
fax: 212-366-4454
e-mail: rmg@robertmillergallery.com
web: www.robertmillergallery.com

Betsy Wittenborn Miller
Robert Peter Miller
Royce Howes

Hours: Tuesday - Saturday 10-6

Works in all media by Modern and Contemporary artists

Artists Exhibited
Diane Arbus
Bill Henson
Walter Niedermayr
Patti Smith
Mayumi Terada

Works by
Ai Weiwei
Berenice Abbott
Eugene Atget
Brassaï
Cecil Beaton
Horace Bristol
Renée Cox
Walker Evans
Ola Kolehmainen
Clarence John Laughlin
George Platt Lynes
Herbert List
Patricia Piccinini
Man Ray
Magritte
Pierson
David Salle
Stanislaw Ignacy Witkiewicz

Sze Tsung Leong, *Beizhuanzi II, Siming District, Xiamen*, 2004
C-Print

Yossi Milo Gallery

525 West 25th Street
New York, NY 10001

tel: 212-414-0370
fax: 212-414-0371
e-mail: mail@yossimilo.com
web: www.yossimilo.com

Yossi Milo, Owner
Alissa Schoenfeld, Director

Hours: Tuesday - Saturday 10-6

Contemporary Art Specializing in Photography

Adam Bartos
Kelli Connell
Tierney Gearon
David Goldes
Sarah Hobbs
Pieter Hugo
Simen Johan
Eirik Johnson
Sze Tsung Leong
Loretta Lux

Martina Mullaney
Nicholas Nixon
Nicholas Prior
Richard Renaldi
Alessandra Sanguinetti
Lise Sarfati
Katherine Turczan
Takashi Yasumura
Kohei Yoshiyuki
Liu Zheng

Walker Evans, *House with Cast Iron Grill Work, New Orleans*, 1936
Gelatin silver print

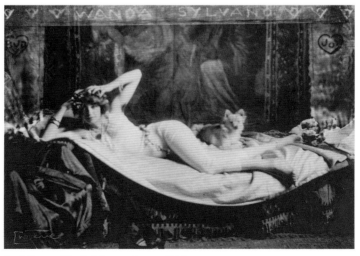

Frank Eugene, *Wanda Sylvano, actress*, c. 1910
Platinum print with applied watercolor

Richard Moore Photographs

PO Box 16245
Oakland, CA 94610

tel: 510-271-0149
fax: 510-645-1194
e-mail: rdmphoto@earthlink.net
web: www.richardmoorephoto.com

Richard D. Moore

Hours: By Appointment

Fine Vintage Photographs from the 19th and 20th Centuries

Berenice Abbott	Johan Hagemeyer	Paul Strand
Ansel Adams	Lewis Hine	Edward Steichen
Laura Adams Armer	Gertrude Kasebier	Alfred Stieglitz
Brassaï	Dorothea Lange	Karl Struss
Anne Brigman	Russell Lee	I.W. Taber
Wynn Bullock	Baron Adolph de Meyer	John Vachon
Alvin Langdon Coburn	William Mortensen	Willard Van Dyke
Will Connell	Eadweard Muybridge	A. C. Vroman
Imogen Cunningham	Sonya Noskowiak	Carleton Watkins
William E. Dassonville	Gordon Parks	Brett Weston
Frank Eugene	Eliot Porter	Edward Weston
Frederick H. Evans	Constant Puyo	Clarence White
Walker Evans	George Rodger	Minor White
Robert Frank	Arthur Rothstein	Willard E. Worden
William Garnett	Peter Sekaer	Max Yavno
Arnold Genthe	Ben Shahn	

Ruth Bernhard, *Magnolia Leaves*, 1952
Vintage

Imogen Cunningham, *Magnolia Blossom*, c. 1925

Scott Nichols Gallery

49 Geary Street, Suite 415
San Francisco, CA 94108

tel: 415-788-4641
fax: 415-788-8438
e-mail: sngphoto@pacbell.net
web: www.scottnicholsgallery.com

Scott Nichols

Hours: Tuesday - Saturday 10:30-5
And By Appointment

19th, 20th Century and Contemporary Photographs

Berenice Abbott	Dr. Harold Edgerton	Sanford Roth
Ansel Adams	William Garnett	Pentti Sammallahti
Kiichi Asano	Group f-64	Unai San Martin
Bruce Bellas (a.k.a. Bruce of LA)	Johan Hagemeyer	Aaron Siskind
Ruth Bernhard	Chester Higgins	Michael A. Smith
Anne Brigman	Rolfe Horn	W. Eugene Smith
Wynn Bullock	Gyorgy Kepes	Peter Stackpole
Harry Callahan	André Kertész	Lynn Stern
Henri Cartier-Bresson	Paul Kozal	Paul Strand
Paul Caponigro	Vilem Kriz	Jock Sturges
Benjamen Chinn	Mona Kuhn	Brad Temkin
Ron Church	Koichiro Kurita	Edmund Teske
Imogen Cunningham	Dorothea Lange	George Tice
Edward S. Curtis	Danny Lyon	Arthur Tress
Andre Cypriano	James Nicholls	Carleton Watkins
Judy Dater	Sonya Noskowiak	Brett Weston
Margo Davis	Said Nuseibeh	Edward Weston
Detroit Photochrome Co.	Irving Penn	Minor White
Monica Denevan	Michael Rauner	and many others

Ruth Bernhard, *In the Box, Horizontal*, 1962

© William Christenberry, *Double Cola Sign, Beale Street, Memphis*, 1966

Pace/MacGill Gallery

32 East 57th Street, 9th Floor
New York, NY 10022

tel: 212-759-7999
fax: 212-759-8964
e-mail: info@pacemacgill.com
web: www.pacemacgill.com

Peter MacGill
Kimberly Jones
Lauren Panzo
Irene Papanestor
Amanda Bowker

Hours: Tuesday - Friday 9:30-5:30
Saturday 10-6

19th, 20th Century and Contemporary Photography

Dieter Appelt
David Byrne
Harry Callahan
William Christenberry
Chuck Close
Philip-Lorca diCorcia
Jim Dine
Walker Evans
Robert Frank
Jim Goldberg
Emmet Gowin
Lauren Greenfield

Robert Heinecken
Mark Klett
Josef Koudelka
Jocelyn Lee
Duane Michals
Diana Michener
Boris Mikhailov
Richard Misrach
Tod Papageorge
Irving Penn
Robert Rauschenberg
Judith Joy Ross

Paolo Roversi
Michal Rovner
Lucas Samaras
Fazal Sheikh
Kiki Smith
Frederick Sommer
Alfred Stieglitz
John Szarkowski
JoAnn Verburg
Andy Warhol
William Wegman
Garry Winogrand

August Sander, *"Krone" at Ring Street, Cologne*, 1930
Vintage silver print

Galerie Priska Pasquer

Goebenstrasse 3
Cologne, 50672, Germany

tel: 49-221-952-6313
fax: 49-221-952-6373
email: galerie@priskapasquer.de
web: www.priskapasquer.de

Priska Pasquer
Ferdinand Brueggemann

Hours: Tuesday - Friday 1-6

**Specializes in Photography of the 1920s, 1930s and
1950s, as well as Contemporary and Japanese Art**

Bauhaus photography	Valentina Kulagina	August Sander
Erwin Blumenfeld	Achim Lippoth	Osamu Shiihara
Rudolf Bonvie	El Lissitzky	Christian Skrein
Dawid	Werner Mantz	Elfriede Stegemeyer
Frantisek Drtikol	F.T. Marinetti	Otto Steinert
Heinz Hajek-Halke	Andrei Molodkin	Josef Sudek
Grit Kallin-Fischer	Daido Moriyama	Hiroshi Sugimoto
Rinko Kawauchi	Enrico Prampolini	Tato
André Kertész	Albert Renger-Patzsch	Umbo
Gustav Klutsis	Alexander Rodchenko	Carola Vogt/Peter Boerboom
Annelise Kretschmer	Jaroslav Rössler	
Germaine Krull	Michael Ruetz	

Camille Corot, *Les arbres dans la montagne (LD 60)*, 1856

Galerie Françoise Paviot

57 rue Sainte-Anne
Paris, 75002, France

tel: 33-1-42-60-10-01
fax: 33-1-42-60-44-77
e-mail: info@paviotfoto.com
web: www.paviotfoto.com

Françoise Paviot
Alain Paviot

Hours: Thursday - Saturday 2:30-7

**19th and 20th Century Fine Vintage
& Contemporary Photographs**

Eugène Atget	Charles Marville	Gilles Gerbaud
Edouard Baldus	L. Moholy-Nagy	Angela Grauerholz
Guy Bourdin	Eadweard Muybridge	Bogdan Konopka
Constantin Brancusi	Charles Nègre	Ann Mandelbaum
Brassaï	René-Jacques	Ray K. Metzker
Henri Cartier-Bresson	Wols	Jürgen Nefzger
Robert Doisneau	Jocelyne Alloucherie	Antoine Poupel
Raymond Hains	Dieter Appelt	Mark Ruwedel
Germaine Krull	A+B Blume	Toshio Shibata
Eli Lotar	Blanca Casas Brullet	R. Thorne-Thomsen
Man Ray	Barbara Crane	Nancy Wilson-Pajic

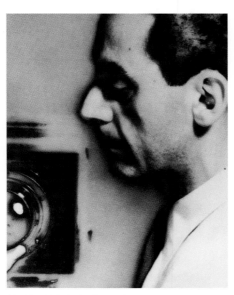

Man Ray, *Solarised self portrait*, 1932
n°25 in our catalogue "Man Ray Forever"

Heinz Hajek-Halke, *Herbst*, c. 1932
Vintage gelatin silver print, montage 22.8 x 17.2 centimeters

PhotoArt

Rathausstrasse 13 / V
Hamburg, 20095, Germany

tel: 49-40-460-1782
fax: 49-40-460-1783
e-mail: erma@photo-art-hamburg.de
web: www.photo-art-hamburg.de

Erma Schmidt-Staerz, Director

Hours: By Appointment

PhotoArt has specialised in 20th century vintage photography with an emphasis on fotoform.
PhotoArt offers touring exhibitions, and portfolios.

Collectors Prints
Subjektive fotografie:*
Kilian Breier
F.C. Gundlach
Heinz Hajek-Halke
Ruth Hallensleben
Peter Keetman
Siegfried Lauterwasser
Adolf Lazi
Herbert List
Pim van Os
Toni Schneiders
Otto Steinert
Ludwig Windstosser

Elliott Erwitt
Konrad Helbig
Thomas Hoepker
Will McBride
Albert Renger-Patzsch
Werner Rohde
Walter Schels
Paul Wolff

Portfolios
Erwin Blumenfeld
Peter Keetman
Karl Struss

* ref. to the exhibition
MoMa SanFrancisco 1984

Neal Slavin, *Channel Swimmers*, 1984

Photographs Do Not Bend Gallery

1202 Dragon Street, Suite 103
Dallas, TX 75207

tel: 214-969-1852
fax: 214-745-9901
e-mail: info@pdnbgallery.com
web: www.pdnbgallery.com

Burt Finger, Gallery Director
Missy Smith Finger, Director
Jennifer Fluegge, Assistant Director

Hours: Tuesday - Saturday 11-6

20th Century and Contemporary Photography by American, Latin American, European and Asian Artists

Representing
John Albok
Jesse Alexander
Stuart Allen
Keith Carter
Joy Christiansen
Don Donaghy
David Graham
William Greiner
Misty Keasler
Michael Kenna
George Krause
Chema Madoz
Delilah Montoya
Morten Nilsson
Michael O'Brien
Bill Owens
Esteban Pastorino Diaz
Marta Maria Perez Bravo
Jeffrey Silverthorne
Neal Slavin
Jock Sturges
Cassio Vasconcellos
Chris Verene

Additional Works by
Lola Alvarez Bravo
Carlotta Corpron
Edward S. Curtis
Jack Delano
Harold Edgerton
Morris Engle
Elliott Erwitt
Flor Garduno
Luis Gonzalez Palma

Earlie Hudnall Jr.
Bohn Chang Koo
Ida G. Lansky
Barbara Maples
Angus McBean
Nickolas Muray
Eliot Porter
William Rittase
Lorry Salcedo
John Stryker

Bill Owens, *Our House Was Built with the Living Room in Back*, 1971

Tazio Secchiaroli, *Federico Fellini on the set of 8 ¹/₂, Cinecittà*, 1962
Unique vintage signed print

Mario Giacomelli, *I Have No Hands To Caress My Face*, 1961-1963
Extra-large signed print

Photology

Via della Moscova. 25
Milan, 20121, Italy

tel: 39-02-659-5285
fax: 39-02-65-4284
e-mail: photology@photology.com
web: www.photology.com

Davide Faccioli, Director

Hours: Tuesday - Saturday 11-7
And By Appointment

At the Photography Show
XX: ITALIANS DO IT BETTER:
Gian Paolo Barbieri
Mario De Biasi
Angelo Frontoni
Luigi Ghirri
Mario Giacomelli
Tina Modotti
Carlo Mollino
Ugo Mulas
Federico Patellani
Tazio Secchiaroli
Eda Urbani
Franco Vaccari

Works by
Nobuyoshi Araki
Richard Avedon
Gian Paolo Barbieri
Henri Cartier-Bresson
Loris Cecchini
Giacomo Costa
William Eggleston
Ron Galella
Luigi Ghirri
Mario Giacomelli
Ilkka Halso
Pertti Kekarainen
David LaChapelle
Dinh Q.Lê

Janne Lehtinen
Kurt Markus
Richard Misrach
Ugo Mulas
Helmut Newton
Riitta Päiväläinen
Jyrki Parantainen
Irving Penn
Jack Pierson
Alexander Rodchenko
Tazio Secchiaroli
Andres Serrano
Ettore Sottsass
Paul Thuile
Joel-Peter Witkin

Luigi Ghirri, *Marina di Ravenna,* 1971
Unique vintage master color print

© Bernard Faucon, *Le Petit Bouddha*

Picture Photo Space, Inc.

Shouto Bldg., 2F
1-8-9 Nishi-Sinsaibashi
Chuo-ku, Osaka 542-0086, Japan

tel: 81-6-6251-3225
fax: 81-6-6251-3245
e-mail: yhy12636@nifty.com
web: www.picturephotospace.com

Masato Aino, Director

Hours: Monday - Saturday 1-6
And By Appointment

Established in 1984. Contemporary Japanese photographers and selected photographers from the United States and Europe.

Jun Abe*	Diane Arbus
Nobuyoshi Araki	E. J. Bellocq
Eikoh Hosoe	Olivier Christinat*
Norifumi Inada*	Larry Clark
Kunihiko Katsumata*	Bernard Faucon
Kazuo Kitai	Lee Friedlander
Michiko Kon	Michael Kenna
Yasuko Kotani*	Sally Mann
Daido Moriyama	Joel Meyerowitz
Takashi Nakagawa*	Olivia Parker
Hiroshi Osaka*	Malcom Pasley
Hiro Sato*	Eliot Porter
Tomio Seike	August Sander
Issei Suda	William Wegman
Hitoshi Tsukiji	Joel-Peter Witkin
Shouji Ueda	Camera Notes & Camera Work
	and others

*Exclusive Representative

Robert Frank, *New York, 1947*
Vintage silver print, 240 x 188 millimeters
Signed on the back

Serge Plantureux

4 Galerie Vivienne
Paris, 75002, France

tel: 33-1-53-29-92-00
fax: 33-1-47-03-08-85
e-mail: info@sergeplantureux.fr
web: www.sergeplantureux.fr

Serge Plantureux
Anne-Rose de Fontainieu
Jean-Mathieu Martini
Matthias Olmeta
Adnan Sezer

Bookshop Hours: Tuesday - Saturday 1-6
Printroom Hours: By Appointment

19th & 20th Century Photography

Periodical on photography collecting: Carnets de Rhinoceros jr (70 euros per 10 issues, oversea)

Eugene Atget	Raoul Hausmann
Edouard Baldus	Edmond Lebel
Giacomo Caneva	Rene Ledoux-Lebard
Henri Cartier-Bresson	Man Ray
Camille Corot	Georges Melies
Eugene Disderi	Wright Morris
Robert Doisneau	Matthias Olmeta
Maxime du Camp	Auguste Rodin
Charles Famin	Tazio Secchiaroli
Robert Frank	Boris Smelov
Mario Giacomelli	Luke Swank
Manuel H	

Mitch Epstein, *Tag Sale III*, 2000
Chromogenic Print

Yancey Richardson Gallery

535 West 22nd Street
New York, NY 10011

tel: 646-230-9610
fax: 646-230-6131
e-mail: info@yanceyrichardson.com
web: www.yanceyrichardson.com

Yancey Richardson
David Carmona
Tracey Norman

Hours: Tuesday - Saturday 10-6

20th Century and Contemporary Photography

Jessica Backhaus	Jodie Vicenta Jacobson	Sebastião Salgado
Lewis Baltz	Kenneth Josephson	Vicki Sambunaris
Olivo Barbieri	Kahn/Selesnick	August Sander
Jeffrey Becom	Nadav Kander	Lynn Saville
Henri Cartier-Bresson	Yousuf Karsh	Sarah Schorr
Chan Chao	Lisa Kereszi	Julius Shulman
Linda Connor	André Kertész	Mike Smith
Jim Cooke	Masotomo Kuriya	Mark Steinmetz
Mario Cravo Neto	Laura Letinsky	Susan Unterberg
Mitch Epstein	Esko Männikkö	Bertien van Manen
Terry Evans	Mary Ellen Mark	Hellen van Meene
Lynn Geesaman	Andrew Moore	Todd Webb
David Hilliard	Christian Patterson	Masao Yamamoto
Tom Hunter	Ed Ruscha	

Todd Hido, *Untitled, #1447-a*, 1996

RoseGallery

2525 Michigan Avenue, G-5
Santa Monica, CA 90404

tel: 310-264-8440
fax: 310-264-8443
e-mail: info@rosegallery.net
web: www.rosegallery.net

Rose Shoshana
Laura Peterson
Hannah Sloan
Andy Stolarek
Molly Toberer
Nicole Katz

Hours: Tuesday - Saturday 10-6

20th Century and Contemporary Works on Paper

Representing
Manuel Álvarez Bravo
Adam Bartos
Virginia Beahan
Bruce Davidson
Jim Dow
William Eggleston
Robbert Flick
Todd Hido
Evelyn Hofer
Birney Imes
Graciela Iturbide
Dorothea Lange
Laura McPhee
Susan Meiselas
Pablo Ortiz Monasterio
Martin Parr
Robert Polidori
Guy Stricherz: Americans in
   Kodachrome 1945-1965
Joaquin Trujillo
Camilo José Vergara
Seung Woo Back

Works by
Diane Arbus
Mark Cohen
Götz Diergarten
Lise Sarfati
Albrecht Tübke
The John Hinde Photographers
from Butlin's Holiday Camps:
   Elmar Ludwig
   Edmund Nägele
   David Noble

Harry Warnecke (attrib.), *Ted Williams, Boston Red Sox*, 1949
TriCarbro Print

BOOTH #217

Richard T. Rosenthal

4718 Springfield Avenue
Philadelphia, PA 19143

tel: 215-726-5493
fax: 215-726-5926
e-mail: rtrphoto@vernacularphotography.com
web site: www.vernacularphotography.com

Richard T. Rosenthal
Janet Shilling

Hours: By Appointment

We offer photographic treasures from the glorious nineteenth century, images by twentieth century masters, and a delightful and eclectic body of vernacular photographs.

James Abbe (1883-1973)
Berenice Abbott (1898-1991)
Jose Alemany
Albert Arthur Allen (1886-1962)
Paul L. Anderson
Edouard Denis Baldus
Cecil Beaton (1904-1980)
A. Aubrey Bodine (1906-1970)
Alice Boughton (1866-1943)
Clarence Sinclair Bull (1869-1979)
Samuel Capuano
Carpenter
Civil War Photographs
Ralston Crawford (1906-1978)
Asahel Curtis (1868-1941)
Edward S. Curtis (1868-1952)
Rudolf Eickemeyer Jr. (1862-1932)
Harry Ellis
Frederick Evans (1853-1943)
Charles Famin

Godfrey Frankel
C.D. Fredericks (1823-1894)
Elmer Fryer
Lena Scott Harris
Hill & Adamson
John R. Hogan (1888-1965)
E.O. Hoppe (1878-1972)
Karl Jan Hora
George Hurrell (1904-1992)
William Henry Jackson
   (1843-1942)
Jan Lauschmann (1901-1991)
Fay Sturtevant Lincoln
Angus McBean (1904-1990)
Karl Moon (1878-1948)
Nickolas Muray (1892-1965)
Carlo Naya
Eliot Porter (1901-1990)
J.B. Rich
Frederick DeBourg Richards

Robert Yarnell Richie
Leni Riefenstahl (1902-2003)
William Rittase (1894-1968)
Ben Shahn (1898-1969)
Clara Sipprell
Edward Steichen (1879-1973)
Josef Sudek (1896-1976)
H.Y. Summons
Lloyd Ullberg
George H. Van Anda
Vernacular Photographs
Vivex Prints
Harry Warnecke (1900-1984)
Todd Webb (1905-2000)
Weegee (1899-1968)
Brett Weston (1911-1993)
Garry Winogrand (1928-1984)
Josef Wondrak
World War II Photographs
Count Zichy

Didier Massard, *Rhinoceros*, 2004
Chromogenic print, 72 x 90 inches, edition of 5

Julie Saul Gallery

535 West 22nd Street, 6th Floor
New York, NY 10011

tel: 212-627-2410
fax: 212-627-2411
e-mail: mail@saulgallery.com
web site: www.saulgallery.com

Julie Saul
Edna Cardinale
Lisa Fontana

Hours: Tuesday - Saturday 11-6
And By Appointment

Founded in 1984, the Julie Saul Gallery specializes in contemporary photography and works
on paper.

Andrew Bordwin
Andrew Bush
Maria Magdalena Campos-Pons
Chien-Chi Chang
Roz Chast
Elaine Lustig Cohen
Julie Evans
J. Bennett Fitts
Sally Gall
Luigi Ghirri
Bill Jacobson
Sarah Anne Johnson
Maira Kalman
Shai Kremer
Reiner Leist

Jeff Chien-Hsing Liao
Birgitta Lund
Neeta Madahar
Maria Martinez-Cañas
Didier Massard
Karin Apollonia Müller
John O'Reilly
Gonzalo Puch
Orit Raff
Gary Schneider
David Stephenson
Iain Stewart
Arne Svenson
Brian Ulrich

N. W. Gibbons, *Equalization*, 2006
Tintype

William L. Schaeffer/ Photographs

PO Box 296
Chester, CT 06412

tel: 860-526-3870

William L. Schaeffer, Director
Arthur Weisenburger, Assistant Director

Hours: Monday - Friday 10-5
And By Appointment

Established in 1974, William L. Schaeffer/Photographs deals in a wide range of nineteenth and twentieth century photographs and daguerreotypes, with a particular emphasis on vintage works of exceptional visual and physical quality. We also represent the contemporary tintype work of N. W. Gibbons.

Fratelli Alinari
Edouard Baldus
Adolphe Braun
George N. Barnard
William Bell
James Wallace Black
Cartes-de-visite
Francis Edmond Currey
Eugene Cuvelier
Daguerreotypes
Maxime DuCamp
Roger Fenton
Hand-Colored Photographs
Hill & Adamson
John K. Hillers
William Henry Jackson
Gustave LeGray
John Moran
Eadweard Muybridge
Timothy O'Sullivan
Andrew Joseph Russell
Charles Scowen
Camille Silvy
Southworth and Hawes
Stereoviews
Isaiah West Taber
Felix Teynard
John Thomson
Tintypes
Tintypes / hand-colored
Carleton Watkins

Eugene Atget
Alvin Langdon Coburn
Edward S. Curtis
Gertrude Kasebier
Heinrich Kuhn
Edwin Hale Lincoln
August Loeffler
Karl Moon
William B. Post
Richard Riley
George Seeley
William Gordon Shields
Edward Steichen
Alfred Stieglitz
Paul Strand
Karl Struss
Clarence H. White
Camera Work

Berenice Abbott
Ansel Adams
Margaret Bourke-White
Bill Brandt
Manuel Alvarez Bravo
Anne Brigman
Wynn Bullock
Harry Callahan
Walker Evans
Robert Frank
N. W. Gibbons
Johan Hagemeyer
Bert Hardy
Lewis Hine
André Kertész
Dorothea Lange
Laszlo Moholy-Nagy
Aaron Siskind
W. Eugene Smith
Doris Ulmann
Carl Van Vechten
Weegee
Brett Weston
Edward Weston
Minor White
and others

Manuel Alvarez Bravo, *El Trapo Negro*, 1986
Vintage gelatin silver print

Edward Weston, *Nude,*1927
Gelatin silver print, Edward Weston/Cole Weston

Scheinbaum & Russek Ltd.

369 Montezuma, #345
Santa Fe, NM 87501

tel: 505-988-5116
fax: 505-988-4346
e-mail: srltd@photographydealers.com
web: www.photographydealers.com

Janet Russek, Director
David Scheinbaum, Director
Sharon Russell, Administrative Assistant

Hours: By Appointment

Established in 1980. Scheinbaum & Russek possess a rare combination of expertise as private dealers, educators, and photographers. Influenced by Beaumont Newhall and Eliot Porter, they continue the tradition, commitment and passion for the photographic medium.

Berenice Abbott
Ansel Adams
Michael Berman
Joseph Beuys
Edouard Boubat
Bill Brandt
Manuel Alvarez Bravo
Wynn Bullock
Harry Callahan
Camera Work Gravures
Paul Caponigro
Manuel Carrillo
Henri Cartier-Bresson
Walter Chappell
William Clift
John Dugdale
Lynn Geesaman
Laura Gilpin
Alex Harris
André Kertész
O. Winston Link
Beaumont Newhall
Nancy Newhall
Luis González Palma
Olivia Parker
Eliot Porter
Janet Russek
Sebastião Salgdao

David Scheinbaum
Aaron Siskind
Ralph Steiner
Alfred Stieglitz
Willard Van Dyke
Todd Webb
Brett Weston
Edward Weston
Minor White
and others

Representing the Estates of
Beaumont and Nancy Newhall
Eliot Porter

Bill Brandt, *Nude, Campden Hill, London, 1949*
Gelatin silver print

Newcomer's Gallery, *Portrait of George B. Lee with Rifle, Philadelphia, PA*, 1857
Ambrotype, 4.5 x 5.5 inches

Anonymous (Japanese), *Three Young Men*, c. 1875
Ambrotype, 3.5 x 4.5 inches in Original Kiri-Wood Case

Charles Schwartz Ltd.

21 East 90th Street
New York, NY 10128

tel: 212-534-4496
fax: 212-534-0313
e-mail: cms@cs-photo.com
web: www.cs-photo.com

Charles Schwartz
Annick Rosenfield

Hours: By Appointment

19th and 20th Century Photographs

Specializing in 19th and 20th Century Photography. Please visit our website to see over 1,000 photographs.

Berenice Abbott
Felice A. Beato
Margaret Bourke-White
Manuel Alvarez Bravo
Henri Cartier-Bresson
Frantisek Drtikol
Andreas Feininger
Harold Feinstein
Roger Fenton
Lee Friedlander
Francis Frith
Shinzo Fukuhara
Herb Gehr
Samuel Gottscho
Shi Guorui
Phillippe Halsman

Fritz Henle
David Ovtavius Hill &
Robert Adamson
Lewis Hine
Charles Hoff
Taikichi Irie
William Henry Jackson
André Kertész
Russell Lee
Charles Lummis
Dr. John Murray
Eadweard Muybridge
NASA
W. Eugene Smith
James Thrall Soby
Ralph Steiner

Joel Sternfeld
Karl Struss
Harry Warnecke
Todd Webb
Mariana Yampolsky
Japanese Pictorialists
& Modernists
Japanese Ambrotypes
Daguerreotypes
19th Century New York City
20th Century New York City
Japanese Propaganda
photographs

Man Ray, *Violon d'Ingres with Strings (Collage)*, 1965
Signed & numbered 1/3 recto on mat
Image: 38.4 x 27.9 centimeters, Mat: 64.8 x 50.2 centimeters

Michael Senft / Masterworks

PO Box 3117
East Hampton, NY 11937

tel: 631-907-0904
fax: 631-907-9795
e-mail: michaelsenft@optonline.net

Michael Senft

Hours: By Appointment

Vintage Surreal Photography

We are private dealers specializing in vintage Man Ray photographs + objects. We also have a select inventory of works by other surrealists.

Man Ray
Kertesz
Lerner
Richter
Tabard
Zwart

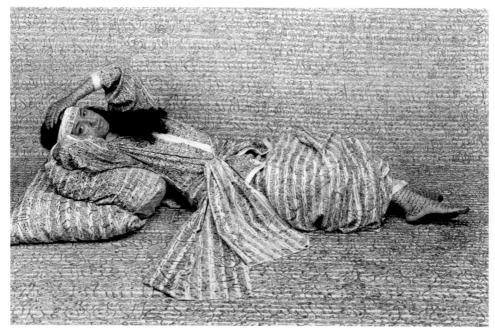

Lalla Essaydi, *Les Femmes du Maroc #16*, 2006
C-print, 30 x 40 inches or 48 x 60 inches

Lisa Sette Gallery

4142 North Marshall Way
Scottsdale, AZ 85251

tel: 480-990-7342
fax: 480-970-0825
e-mail: sette@lisasettegallery.com
web: www.lisasettegallery.com

Lisa Sette, Director
Duane D. Smith, Associate Director
Ashley Rice, Director of Photography
Michael Mulno, Special Projects
Helen E. Raleigh, Web Mistress
Elena Lourenco, Preparator

Hours: Tuesday - Friday 10-5, Thursday evenings 7-9
Saturday 12-5

For over 20 years Lisa Sette Gallery has consistently challenged the notion of what contemporary photography can be with a vision that is personal – a visual voice that is relevant to the times in which we live.

Karl Blossfeldt
Alain Gerard Clement
Binh Danh
Lalla Essaydi
Luis Gonzalez Palma
Rimma Gerlovina /
 Valeriy Gerlovin
Rick Hards
Nissa Kubly
Kahn/Selesnick
Mark Klett
David Levinthal
Chema Madoz
Marie Navarre
Maurizio Pellegrin
RES
Julianne Swartz
Mike & Doug Starn
James Turrell
Ian Van Coller
William Wegman
Jo Whaley

Rick Hards, *Mandrake*, 2006
Oil on tintype mounted on wood panel
17 x 15 inches, unique

Pirkle Jones, *Dice, Flea Market, Marin City, California (1976)*
Vintage gelatin silver print

Michael Shapiro Photographs

49 Geary Street, Suite 208
San Francisco, CA 94108

tel: 415-398-6655
fax: 415-398-0667
e-mail: info@shapirogallery.net
web: www.shapirogallery.net

Michael Shapiro, Owner
Enrico Cittadino

Hours: By Appointment

Dealers since 1980

Berenice Abbott
Ansel Adams
Ruth Bernhard
Ilse Bing
Margaret Bourke-White
Horace Bristol
Steven Brock
Esther Bubley
Henri Cartier-Bresson
Mark Citret
Imogen Cunningham
Scott Davis
Alfred Eisenstaedt
Walker Evans
Robert Frank
Lyle Gomes

William Gottlieb
John Gutmann
Johan Hagemeyer
Jefferson Hayman
William Heick
Lewis Hine
Kenro Izu
Pirkle Jones
Gyorgy Kepes
André Kertész
Stefan Kirkeby
Josef Koudelka
Dorothea Lange
Jason Langer
Alma Lavenson

Dorothy Norman
Sonya Noskowiak
Irving Penn
Sebastião Salgado
Rocky Schenck
Joe Schwartz
Aaron Siskind
W. Eugene Smith
Edward Steichen
Paul Strand
Weegee
Brett Weston
Edward Weston
John Wimberley
Marion Post Wolcott

E. O. Hoppé, *Middletown in the Snow, Connecticut*, 1926
Vintage gelatin silver print

Silverstein Photography

535 West 24th Street
New York, NY 10011

tel: 212-627-3930
fax: 212-691-5509
e-mail: inquiries@silversteinphotography.com
web: www.silversteinphotography.com

Bruce Silverstein
Elizabeth Shank
Liam Derik van Loenen
Luis Escalera
Yvonne Gomez

Hours: Tuesday - Saturday 11-6

Representing
Estate of Robert Doisneau
Leonard Freed
Bruce Gilden
Estate of Ernst Haas
Estate of E. O. Hoppé
Estate of André Kertész
Nathan Lyons
Barbara Morgan Archive
Marvin Newman
The Frank Paulin Archive
Larry Silver
Sarah Stolfa
Zoe Strauss
Ryan Weideman
Joel-Peter Witkin

Select Works
Diane Arbus
Atget
Ilse Bing
Constantin Brancusi
Bill Brandt
Brassaï
Harry Callahan
Henri Cartier-Bresson
Imogen Cunningham
F Holland Day
Frantisek Drtikol
Frederick Evans
Walker Evans
Robert Frank
Lee Friedlander
Mario Giacomelli
Florence Henri
Rudolf Koppitz
Dorothea Lange
Helen Levitt
Danny Lyon
Rene Magritte
Man Ray
Werner Mantz

Henry Moore
Paul Outerbridge
Irving Penn
Albert Renger-Patzsch
Alexander Rodchenko
Christian Schad
Ben Shahn
Charles Sheeler
Arthur Siegel
Aaron Siskind
W. Eugene Smith
Edward Steichen
Alfred Steiglitz
Sarah Stolfa
Paul Strand
Karl Struss
Umbo
Andy Warhol
Weegee
Brett Weston
Randy West
Edward Weston
Clarence White
Minor White
Garry Winogrand

Edward Weston, *Kelp, Point Lobos*, 1939

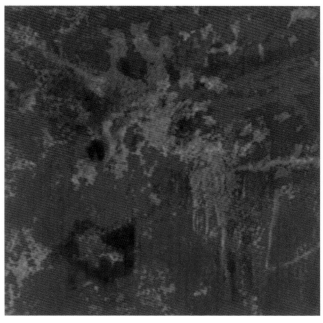

Jack Welpott, *Tri-Color Separation, (Dye Transfer)*, 1980

Barry Singer Gallery

7 Western Avenue
Petaluma, CA 94952

tel: 707-781-3200
fax: 707-781-3030
e-mail: singer@singergallery.com
web: www.singergallery.com

Barry Singer
Gretchen Singer

Hours: Tuesday - Saturday 11-6

Vintage and Contemporary Photographs

Berenice Abbott
Ansel Adams
Eugene Atget
Bruno Barbey
Cara Barer
Jeffrey Becom
Ilse Bing
Margaret Bourke-White
Bill Brandt
Anne Brigman
Wynn Bullock
Larry Colwell
Martin Elkort
Walker Evans
*Irene Fay
Robert Frank
William Garnett

John Gutmann
Philippe Halsman
Dave Heath
Robert Heinecken
Lewis Hine
André Kertész
Vilem Kriz
Joel Levinson
Peter Lippmann
Ken Light
Roger Mayne
Inge Morath
Phil Palmer
Kenneth Parker
Albert Renger-Patzsch
*George Rodger
Arthur Rothstein

Rae Russel
Aaron Siskind
W. Eugene Smith
Herb Snitzer
Peter Stackpole
*Lou Stoumen
Edmund Teske
Lew Thomas
*Lloyd Ullberg
Roman Vishniac
John Vanderpant
Todd Webb
Jack Welpott
Brett Weston
Edward Weston

*Exclusive Estate
Representation

Issac H. Bonsall, *Chattanooga Railroad Yards #1, Tennessee*, c. 1864
Albumen print

Andrew Smith Gallery, Inc.

203 West San Francisco Street
Santa Fe, NM 87501

tel: 505-984-1234
fax: 505-983-2428
e-mail: info@andrewsmithgallery.com
web: www.andrewsmithgallery.com

Andrew Smith, President
John Boland, Associate Director
Christopher Marquez

Hours: Monday - Saturday 10-5

The Andrew Smith Gallery is the world's leading photography gallery selling classic 19th and 20th Century American Photography since 1974. We specialize in important 19th century exploration and ethnographic photography by Alexander Gardner, John Hillers, William Henry Jackson, Edward Muybridge, Andrew J. Russell, Charles R. Savage, Timothy O'Sullivan, Carlton Watkins; important 20th century photography by Ansel Adams, Laura Gilpin, Adam Clark Vroman, Edward Weston; important photographs by Henri Cartier Bresson, Elliott Erwitt, Lee Friedlander, Annie Leibovitz, Herman Leonard

19th Century exploration and ethnographic photography
Alexander Gardner
John Hillers
William Henry Jackson
Edward Muybridge
Andrew J. Russell
Charles R. Savage
Timothy O'Sullivan
Carleton Watkins

20th Century Masters
Ansel Adams
Manuel Alvarez Bravo
Paul Caponigro
Henri Cartier-Bresson
Edward S. Curtis
Elliot Erwitt
Lee Friedlander
Laura Gilpin
Yousuf Karsh
Herman Leonard
Annie Leibovitz
O. Winston Link
Arnold Newman
Eliot Porter
W. Eugene Smith
Edward Steichen
Alfred Stieglitz
Paul Strand
Adam Clark Vroman
Edward Weston

Leonard Misonne (Belgian, 1870-1943), *Pluie à Namur*, c. 1937
Vintage mediobrome print, 11⅜ x 15¼ inches

Joel Soroka Gallery

400 East Hyman Avenue
Aspen, CO 81611

tel: 970-920-3152
fax: 970-920-3823
e-mail: joelsoroka@msn.com

Joel Soroka

Hours: Monday - Saturday 11-6
And By Appointment

Berenice Abbott
Laure Albin-Guillot
Herbert Bayer
Ilse Bing
Blanc and Demilly
Erwin Blumenfeld
Brassaï
Henri Cartier-Bresson
William Dassonville
Robert Doisneau
Frantisek Drtikol
Pierre Dubreuil
Elliott Erwitt
Jaromir Funke
Ralph Gibson
Samuel Gottscho

Johan Hagemeyer
Gyorgy Kepes
Jan Lauschmann
Man Ray
Leonard Misonne
Nicholas Muray
Edward Quigley
Drahomir Ruzicka
Bohumil Stastny
Edward Steichen
Karl Struss
Josef Sudek
Roman Vishniac
Brett Weston
Edward Weston

Contemporary photographers
Tom Baril
Lynn Bianchi
Robert Bianchi
Rod Cook
Franco Donaggio
Lalla Essaydi
Luis Gonzalez-Palma
Cig Harvey
Beatrice Helg
Frederic Ohringer
Dede Reed
Joyce Tenneson
Mandy Vahabzadeh

Melvin Sokolsky, *Fly Dior, Harper's Bazaar, Paris*, 1965

Lillian Bassman, *Margy Cato, Harper's Bazaar*, 1947

Staley+Wise Gallery

560 Broadway, Suite 305
New York, NY 10012

tel: 212-966-6223
fax: 212-966-6293
e-mail: photo@staleywise.com
web: www.staleywise.com

Etheleen Staley, Director
Takouhy Wise, Director

Hours: Tuesday - Saturday 11-5

Slim Aarons
Jesse Alexander
Sid Avery
Peter Basch
Lillian Bassman
Cecil Beaton
Carol Beckwith and
    Angela Fisher
Harry Benson
Nick Brandt
Louise Dahl-Wolfe
Patrick Demarchelier
Andre de Dienes
Robert Doisneau
Michael Dweck
Arthur Elgort
Toni Frissell
Ormond Gigli
Milton Greene
Horst
Frank Horvat
Hoyningen-Heune
George Hurrell
André Kertész
Steven Klein
Daniel Kramer
David LaChapelle
Jaques-Henri Lartigue

Erica Lennard
Kurt Markus
Herbert Matter
Sheila Metzner
Lee Miller
Genevieve Naylor
Helmut Newton
Norman Parkinson
Denis Piel
Len Prince
Rico Puhlmann
Bob Richardson
Herb Ritts
Amalie Rothschild
Jerry Schatzberg
Jeanloup Sieff
Melvin Sokolsky
Edward Steichen
Bert Stern
Phil Stern
John Stewart
Deborah Turbeville
Ellen von Unwerth
Chris von Wangenheim
Alfred Wertheimer
Bob Willoughby
Firooz Zahedi

Horst, *Mainbocher Corset, Paris,* 1939

Imogen Cunningham, *The Unmade Bed*, 1957
Early gelatin silver print, 11 x 14 inches

BOOTH #205

John Stevenson Gallery

338 West 23rd Street
New York, NY 10011-2201

tel: 212-352-0070
fax: 212-741-6449
e-mail: mail@johnstevenson-gallery.com
web: www.johnstevenson-gallery.com

John Stevenson, Director
Will Story, Manager & Curator

Hours: Tuesday - Saturday 11-6

Vintage and contemporary photography

Emphasis on fine handcrafted prints and rare processes.

Vintage & Classic
Ruth Bernhard
Imogen Cunningham
Frederick H. Evans
Arnold Genthe
Bedrich Grünzweig
Vilém Kříž
Heinrich Kühn
George Platt Lynes
Irving Penn
Camera Work

Contemporary
Mark Beard
Linda Broadfoot
Lana Caplan
Brigitte Carnochan

Martha Casanave
Toni Catany
Lucien Clergue
Michael Crouser
Cy DeCosse
Caroline Davies
Marianne Engberg
Joy Goldkind
Joel Grey
John Guider
V. Tony Hauser
Koichiro Kurita
Marcus Leatherdale
Achim Lippoth
Mary Ann Lynch
Michal Macku
John H. Metoyer

Sheila Metzner
Beth Moon
Will Hiroshi & Lisa Oda
Elizabeth Opalenik
Lilo Raymond
Victoria Ryan
Ernestine Ruben
Josephine Sacabo
Vincent Serbin
Hugh Shurley
Philip Trager
Sarah Van Keuren
John Yang
Dimitris Yeros
Zoë Zimmerman

Vilém Kříž, *Collaged Face, Oakland,* 1966
Vintage gelatin silver print, toned, 14 x 11

Cy DeCosse, *White Lotus of the Buddha,* 2006
Dichromate pigments, 20 x 27 inches

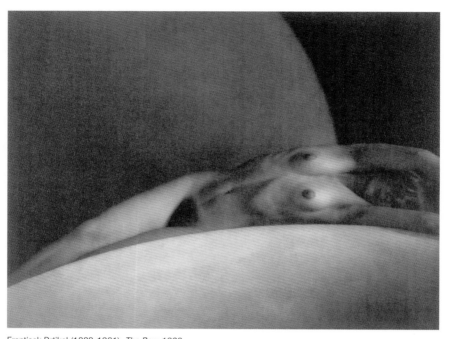

Frantisek Drtikol (1883-1961), *The Bow*, 1928
Vintage pigment print, 8³/₄ x 11¹/₈ inches
Mounted to textured board, signed and dated by the photographer in pencil on the mount,
signed, titled and inscribed with the photographer's address by the photographer in ink and
with an *Internationale Photographische Ausstellung* exhibition label on the reverse, 1928

Galerie Zur Stockeregg

Stockerstrasse 33
Zürich, 8022, Switzerland

tel: 41-44-202-69-25
fax: 41-44-202-82-51
e-mail: info@stockeregg.com
web: www.stockeregg.com

Kaspar M. Fleischmann, Director
Claudia Coellen Helbling, Assistant Director
Beatrice Amstutz, Administration

Hours: Tuesday - Friday 9-6

Twentieth Century Vintage and Contemporary Photographs

Berenice Abbott	Lewis W. Hine	**Contemporary**
Ansel Adams	Stefan Jasienski	Peter Gasser
Eugene Atget	André Kertész	Dorothea Kehaya
Richard Avedon	Heinrich Kuehn	Victor Macarol
Ilse Bing	Gustave Le Gray	Richard Misrach
Margaret Bourke-White	Laszlo Moholy-Nagy	Alfred Seiland
Constantin Brancusi	Paul Outerbridge	Elisabeth Sunday
Bill Brandt	Man Ray	Tanjuci Senji
Brassai	Albert Renger-Patzsch	Dan Weaks
Manuel Alvarez Bravo	Alexander Rodchenko	Rene Zuercher
Rene Burri	Anton Stankowski	
Henri Cartier-Bresson	Edward Steichen	see our website for
Imogen Cunningham	Albert Steiner	further artists
William E. Dassonville	Alfred Stieglitz	
Baron Adolphe de Meyer	Paul Strand	
Frantisek Drtikol	Karl Struss	
Pierre Dubreuil	Josef Sudek	
Walker Evans	Carleton E. Watkins	
Robert Frank	Brett Weston	
Ernst Haas	Edward Weston	

1/2 plate Tinetype, 1870

The Camera makes an Impression:
African-American images 1864-1980
(A Personal Collection)

Religious News Survice, Attica Revolt, 1971

TARTT/washington

1711 Connecticut Avenue, NW
Washington, DC 20009

tel: 202-256-7343
e-mail: jctjr@earthlink.net

Jo C. Tartt, Jr.

Hours: By Appointment

BOOTH
#215

19th Century	**20th Century**
A. Bourne	H. Callahan
G. Barker	R. E. Meatyard
F. Beato	Minor White
Tung-Hing	Nathan Lyons
G. Sommer	Sally Mann
A. Gardner	William Christenberry
E. Baldus	Gundula Schulze
E. Muybridge	Lee Friedlander
Roger Fenton	Stephan Shore
Kimbe	E. Weston
H. P. Robinson	R. Pare
Wm. Saunders	Man Ray
	E. Steichen
	R. Capa
	Francesca Woodman

Thomas Childes

On Offer:
The Tartt/Worswick Collection of
19th Century Chinese Photography

Marilyn Bridges, *Assos, Temple Athena*, 2004
Gelatin silver print

Throckmorton Fine Art, Inc.

145 East 57th Street, 3rd Floor
New York, NY 10022

tel: 212-223-1059
fax: 212-223-1937
e-mail: info@throckmorton-nyc.com
web: www.throckmorton-nyc.com

Spencer Throckmorton, Owner
Kraige Block, Director
Luke Leonard, Photo Registrar/Graphic Designer
Jessica Curnoe, Antiquities Registrar
Sean Cleary, Art Handler

Hours: Tuesday - Saturday 11-5

Throckmorton Fine Art, Inc. is a New York based gallery that specializes in Latin American vintage and contemporary photography, Pre-Columbian Art, and Chinese Jade. The gallery's extraordinary photography collection includes strong works of museum quality by luminaries such as Tina Modotti, Manuel Alvarez-Bravo, Edward Weston, Martin Chambi, and others. The gallery also has an extensive inventory of contemporary photographs, paintings, works on paper, and graphics by Modern and Contemporary Latin American artists.

We also maintain a large selection of male nude images by: Alvin Booth, Arthur Tress, Bauer Sa, Bruce Weber, Bruce of LA, Dianora Niccolini, Edward Muybrige, Ferenc Suto, George Dureau, George Platt Lynes, Gerardo Suter, Hans Fahrmeyer, Joe Lalli, Jonathan Webb, Kelly Grider, Lionel Wendt, Lon of New York, Lorry Salcedo-Mitrani, Lucien Clergue, Luis Mallo, Robert Stivers, Roberto Rincon, Steven Haas, Tom Bianchi, Wilhelm Von Gloeden, et.al.

For further information contact Kraige Block, Director at (212) 223-1059.

Ruven Afanador	Christian Cravo	Dianora Niccolini
Mario Algaze	Mario Cravo Neto	Emmy Lou Packard
Juan Carlos Alom	Valdir Cruz	Luis Gonzalez Palma
Lucienne Bloch	Hector Garcia	Marta Maria Perez Bravo
Lola Alvarez Bravo	Flor Garduno	Antonio Reynoso
Manuel Alvarez Bravo	Baron Wilhelm von Gloeden	Javier Silva Meinel
Hugo Brehme	Fritz Henle	Bernard Silberstein
Marilyn Bridges	Graciela Iturbide	Robert Stivers
Abel Briquet	Guillermo Kahlo	Paul Strand
Anton Bruehl	George Platt Lynes	Laurena Toledo
Henri Cartier-Bresson	Leo Matiz	Bill Perlmutter
Agustin Victor Casasola	Dirk McDonnell	Edward Weston
Martin Chambi	Tina Modotti	Mariana Yampolsky

Paul Strand, *Farm, Valley of the Arc, Haute Savoie, France*, 1950
Signed vintage gelatin silver print

Wach Gallery

31860 Walker Road
Avon Lake, Ohio 44012

tel: 440-933-2780
fax: 440-933-2781
e-mail: mail@wachgallery.com
web: www.wachgallery.com

Peter M. Wach
Judith M. Wach

Hours: By Appointment

Fine Vintage and Contemporary Photographs

Berenice Abbott	William Henry Jackson
Ansel Adams	Yousuf Karsh
Lyle Allan	Robert Glenn Ketchum
Ambrotypes	Andre Kertész
Bill Brandt	Heinrich Kühn
Mathew Brady	The Estate of Barbara Morgan
Brassaï	Willard Morgan
Margaret Bourke-White	Arnold Newman
Wynn Bullock	Timothy O'Sullivan
Camera Work	Eliot Porter
William Carter	Arthur Rothstein
Alvin Langdon Coburn	Andrew Joseph Russell
Imogen Cunningham	W. Eugene Smith
Edward Sheriff Curtis	Edward Steichen
Daguerreotypes	Alfred Stieglitz
Robert Doisneau	Paul Strand
Walker Evans	Frank Meadow Sutcliffe
Neil Folberg	Peter M. Wach
Alexander Gardner	Carleton E. Watkins
Walter Grossman	Brett Weston
Ernst Haas	Cole Weston
Philippe Halsman	Edward Weston
Nicholas Hlobeczy	Clarence White
Carl Austin Hyatt	Minor White

Alec Soth, *Misty*, 2005
Chromogenic print

Weinstein Gallery

908 West 46th Street
Minneapolis, MN 55419

tel: 612-822-1722
fax: 612-822-1745
e-mail: weingall@aol.com
web: www.weinstein-gallery.com

Martin Weinstein
Laura Hoyt, Director

Hours: Tuesday - Saturday 12-5

Weinstein Gallery focuses on modern and contemporary art in all media, with an emphasis on photography. Weinstein Gallery is also a member of the Art Dealers Association of America.

Kelli Connell
Robert Mapplethorpe
McDermott & McGough
Sarah Moon
Luis Gonzalez Palma
Robert Polidori
Nancy Rexroth
Sebastião Salgado
Paul Shambroom
Alec Soth
Mike and Doug Starn

Brandon Herman, *Untitled (Boy in Pool)*, 2006
C-print, 30 x 45 inches, Edition of 5

Wessel + O'Connor Fine Art

111 Front Street, Suite 200
Dumbo Brooklyn, NY 11201

tel: 718-596-1700
fax: 718-596-1764
e-mail: wesseloconnor@aol.com
web: www.wesseloconnor.com

William C. O'Connor
John C. Wessel

Hours: Wednesday - Saturday 11-6

**Fine Art Photography Gallery
in existence for over 20 years**

Steven Arnold
Wouter Deruytter
John Dugdale
Jim French
Greg Gorman
Brandon Herman
John Hinde
Horst P. Horst
George Hoyningen-Huene
Steven Klein
Rudolph Koppitz
Herbert List
Mark Lynch
George Platt Lynes

Robert Mapplethorpe
Bert Morgan
Eadweard Muybridge
PaJaMa
Herb Ritts
Howard Roffman
Luke Smalley
Raymond Voinquel
Wilhelm von Gloeden
Joel-Peter Witkin
50'S PHYSIQUE:
Athletic Model Guild
Bruce of Los Angeles
Western Photo Guild

Hill & Adamson, *Royal Institution & Part of The Castle, Edinburgh*, 1844
Salt print, 7 3/4 x 5 5/8 inches

The Weston Gallery, Inc.

6th Avenue / Dolores and Lincoln
PO Box 655
Carmel, CA 93921

tel: 831-624-4453
fax: 831-624-7190
e-mail: info@westongallery.com
web: www.westongallery.com

Maggi Weston, President
Richard Gadd, Director

Hours: Open Daily 10:30-5:30

Rare Vintage and Contemporary Photographs

19th Century	20th Century	Contemporary
Eugene Atget	Ansel Adams	Jeffrey Becom
Edouard Baldus	Bill Brandt	Linda Butler
Julia Margaret Cameron	Wynn Bullock	Mark Citret
Louis de Clercq	Imogen Cunningham	Rod Dresser
Eugene Cuvelier	Yousuf Karsh	Richard Ehrlich
Frederick H. Evans	André Kertész	Ralph Gibson
Roger Fenton	Robert Mapplethorpe	Chip Hooper
Gustave le Gray	Wright Morris	Rolfe Horn
Charles Marville	Irving Penn	Michael Kenna
Eadweard Muybridge	Man Ray	Paul Kozal
Charles Negre	Edward Steichen	Yoshimitsu Nagasaka
William Henry Fox Talbot	Alfred Stieglitz	Kenneth Parker
Felix Teynard	Paul Strand	Jerry Takigawa
Linnaeus Tripe	Josef Sudek	Maggie Taylor
Carleton Watkins	Brett Weston	Jerry Uelsmann
	Cole Weston	Robert Weingarten
	Edward Weston	

Press Photographer, *Suspected Saboteur*, San Francisco, 1941

Winter Works on Paper

160 Fifth Avenue, #718
New York, NY 10010

tel: 212-352-9013
fax: 718-388-5217
e-mail: winterworks@verizon.net
web: www.winterworksonpaper.com

David Winter

Hours: By Appointment

Many photographers are born in a dumpster and are entombed in a museum, we try to be the middleman.

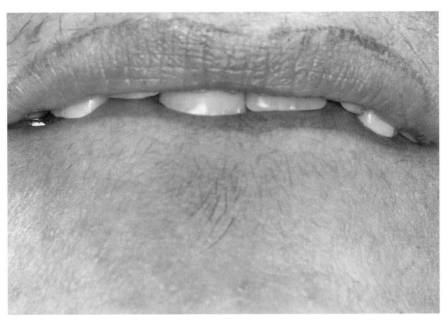

Leonard Hirschfeld, *Dentist*, 1940's

Laurence Demaison, *Aqua bon*, 2006
Gelatin silver print, 16.9 x 22.8 inches

Galerie Esther Woerdehoff

36, rue Falguière
Paris, 75015, France

tel: 33-1-43-21-44-83
fax: 33-1-43-21-45-03
e-mail: galerie@ewgalerie.com
web: www.ewgalerie.com

Esther Woerdehoff
Beatrice Rossetto
Sara Bertilsson

Hours: Tuesday - Saturday 2-6

The photographic gallery was created in 1996 and is specialised in two fields:

1. Photography from the thirties to sixties including prints and vintages of french and american artists (Henri Cartier-Bresson, Edouard Boubat, Frank Horvat, Diana Arbus, Leonard Freed, Elliott Erwitt, Inge Morath).

2. The gallery represents also conceptual photographers like Matthias Koch (student of the Becher's school in Düsseldorf), Laurence Demaison, Loan Nguyen, Marina Gadonneix and Chema Madoz.

The gallery is located in Paris, Montparnasse area, in a historical house where have been working sculptors such as Camille Claudel and Brancusi. During the Second World War, it was a place for a secret printing house for the French Resistance.

In this historic house, the gallery shows 6 exhibitions of photography each year, including monographs and thematic subjects.

Diana Arbus	Pascal Loubet	Henri Cartier-Bresson
Rene Burri	Chema Madoz	Elliott Erwitt
Mario A.	Olivier Meriel	Daniel Frasnay
Mario Cravo Neto	Loan Nguyen	Leonard Freed
Xavier Dauny	Ariel Ruiz i Altaba	Frank Horvat
Laurence Demaison	Arthur Tress	Monique Jacot
Connie Imboden	Michael von Graffenried	Inge Morath
Matthias Koch	Edouard Boubat	Marina Gadonneix

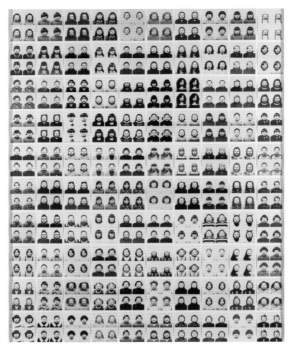

Tomoko Sawada, *ID400 (201-300)*, 1998
100 gelatin silver prints, 51 x 41 inches framed, Edition of 15

Ralston Crawford, *Clams*, c. 1964
Gelatin silver print, 10 x 8 inches

Zabriskie Gallery

41 East 57th Street, 4th Floor
New York, NY 10022

tel: 212-752-1223
fax: 212-752-1224
e-mail: info@zabriskiegallery.com
web: www.zabriskiegallery.com

Virginia Zabriskie, Owner
Alexis Dean, Associate Director
Jonathan Spies, Associate Director

Hours: Tuesday - Saturday 10-5:30

Berenice Abbot
Laure Albin-Guillot
Eugene Atget
Edouard Baldus
John Batho
Felice Beato
Cecil Beaton
Ilse Bing
Erwin Blumenfeld
Edouard Boubat
Pierre Boucher
Marcel Bovis
Brassaï
Harry Callahan
Mark Cohen
Galerie Contemporaine
Konrad Cramer
Ralston Crawford
Edward Curtis
Robert Doisneau
Remy Duval
Mark Feldstein
Joan Fontcuberta
Bisson Freres
Lee Friedlander
Karel Hajek
Raoul Hausmann
Lewis Hine
Izis
Lotte Jacobi

Rene Jacques
Pierre Jahan
Pascal Kern
André Kertész
William Klein
Francois Kollar
Paul Maurer
Wilhelm Maywald
Joel Meyerowitz
Nicholas Nixon
Tod Papageorge
Roger Parry
Guglielmo Pluschow
Man Ray
Albert Renger-Patzsch
Bruno Requillart

Jacques Reutlinger
Jorge Ribalta
Theodore Roszak
Emile Savitry
Tomoko Sawada
Albert Seeberger
Edward Steichen
Alfred Stieglitz
Paul Strand
Patrick Tosani
Gerard Traquandi
Ben Vautier
Baron von Gloeden
Weegee
Garry Winogrand
Rene Zuber

Joan Fontcuberta, *Googlegram 13: UFO*, 2005
C-print, 47 1/4 x 63 inches, Edition of 5

www.plukmagazine.com
info@plukmagazine.com
Telephone +44 (0)20 7839 9300
Fax +44 (0)20 7321 0496

the quarterly photography guide

Interviews //
Features //
Books //
Reviews //
Previews //
Listings //

pluk *magazine*

Issue #31   News, Previews, Auction Report,
Autumn 2006   **Juliet Hacking** *on The Art of Collecting Photography,*
£3.50 €5.00 $6.50   **Roger Ballen, Michael Mack,** Books, Listings

Advertisers

Galleries and Professional Services Relating to the Field of Fine Art Photography

A-2

artnet®

Is it on artnet?

www.artnet.com | www.artnet.de

A-3

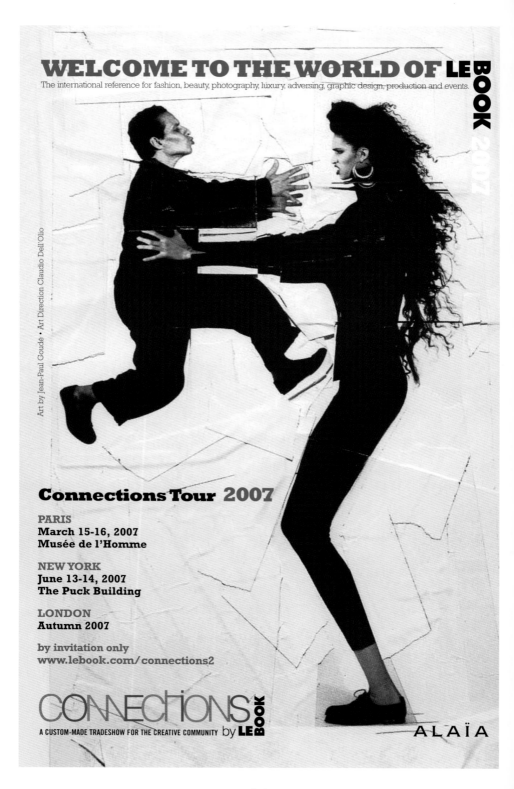

WELCOME TO THE WORLD OF LE BOOK

The international reference for fashion, beauty, photography, luxury, advertising, graphic design, production and events.

LE BOOK 2007

Art by Jean-Paul Goude • Art Direction Claudio Dell'Olio

Connections Tour 2007

PARIS
March 15-16, 2007
Musée de l'Homme

NEW YORK
June 13-14, 2007
The Puck Building

LONDON
Autumn 2007

by invitation only
www.lebook.com/connections2

CONNECTIONS BOOK

A CUSTOM-MADE TRADESHOW FOR THE CREATIVE COMMUNITY by LE BOOK

ALAÏA

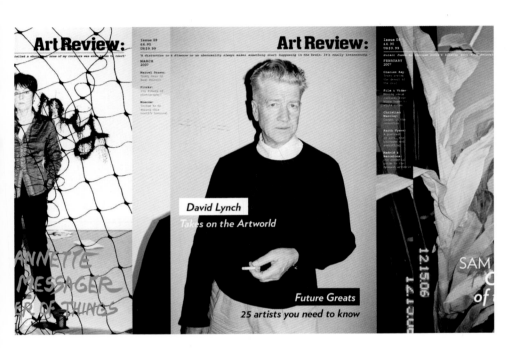

photography

The New Modern:
Pre- and Post-War
Japanese Photography
January 13 – April 1

An Unobserved Life:
Folk Photography
by Joe Schwartz
January 13 – April 1

Ansel Adams over Time:
Recent Photographic
Acquisitions
April 7 – June 23

Made in Santa Barbara:
Contemporary
Photographs
July 1 – October 7

SANTA BARBARA
MUSEUM OF
ART

Santa Barbara Museum of Art
1130 State Street, Santa Barbara, CA 93101
805.963.4364   www.sbma.net
open Tues—Sun, 11 am to 5 pm

Images top to bottom: Hosoe Eikoh, *Kamaitachi #8* (detail), 1965/1997. Gelatin silver print. Santa Barbara Museum of Art, Gift of Arthur B. Steinman. Joe Schwartz, *Tricycle Gang*, 1940s. Gelatin silver print. From the Collection of Joe Schwartz. Ansel Adams, *Lone Pine*, circa 1970. Gelatin silver print. Santa Barbara Museum of Art, Gift of Margaret Weston. ©2007 The Ansel Adams Publishing Rights Trust. Josef Muench, *Fireworks at the Santa Barbara Mission*. Gelatin silver print. Santa Barbara Museum of Art, Gift of Christine Elliot.

ACMS

ARCHIVE CONSULTING AND MANAGEMENT SERVICES LLC

Appraisers of Documentary & Fine Art Photographs

Specializing in Estates, Charitable Donations and Insurance
Appraisals including Digital Collection Management

Robert Gurbo and Sarah Morthland

USPAP Compliant

Eugene Atget / Berenice Abbott
Avenue des Gobelins, 1927

André Kertész
Dalcross Students, Paris, 1930
© Estate of André Kertész

ACMS LLC 511 West 25th Street Suite 609 New York NY 10001
Tel 212-242-7767 Fax 212-242-7797 acms@photoappraisers.com

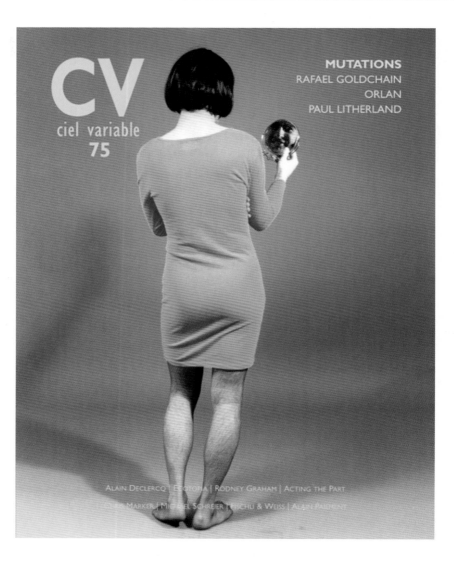

A-8

PHOTOGRAPHS

AUCTIONS NEW YORK
24 EXCEPTIONAL PHOTOGRAPHS 24 APRIL 7pm
PHOTOGRAPHS 25 APRIL 10am and 2pm

Viewing 11 - 24 April

PROPERTY FROM THE COLLECTION OF SOIZIC AUDOUARD

CLAUDE CAHUN *Autoportrait*, 1929 Gelatin silver print, 4 x 3 in. (10.2 x 7.6 cm.)

Estimate $20,000–30,000 To be offered 25 April 2007

Department of Photographs New York +1 212 940 1245
Paris +33 1 42 78 67 77   Berlin +49 30 880 018 42
London +44 20 7318 4018   Munich +49 89 291 34 28
Catalogues +1 212 940 1240

PHILLIPS
de PURY & COMPANY

Phillips de Pury & Company
450 West 15 Street New York www.phillipsdepury.com

Photographs in New York

Man Ray, *Noire et Blanche*
gelatin silver print, 1926, 7 x 9 in. 17.5 x 22.8 cm.
Estimate: $200,000 – 300,000
To be sold in Photographs from the Private Collection of
Margaret W. Weston

Henry Wessel, Jr., *Walapai, Arizona*
gelatin silver print, 1971, printed in the early 1980s
10 ½ x 15 ⅝ in. 26.7 x 39.7 cm.
Estimate: $15,000 – 20,000
To be sold in Photographs

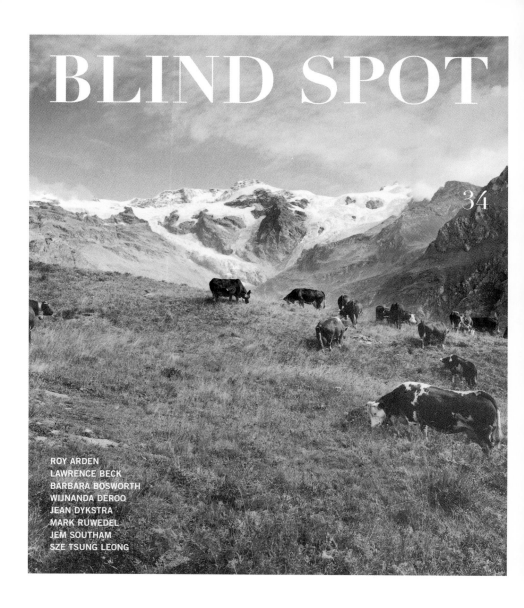

BLIND SPOT

34

ROY ARDEN
LAWRENCE BECK
BARBARA BOSWORTH
WIJNANDA DEROO
JEAN DYKSTRA
MARK RUWEDEL
JEM SOUTHAM
SZE TSUNG LEONG

collect subscribe support

Blind Spot, the Premier Photo-Based Art Magazine
For a complete selection of Limited Edition Prints,
Back Issues, and Books, visit www.blindspot.com.

Blind Spot & Photo-Based Art, Inc. 210 Eleventh Avenue NYC 10001 212.633.1317 blindspot.com
Photo-Based Art, Inc. is a 501 (c) 3 not-for-profit organization

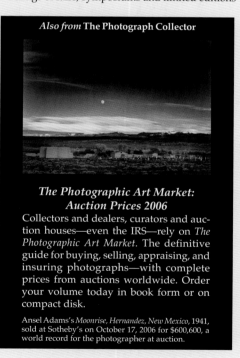

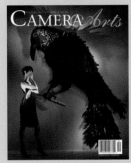  

photo **los angeles**

photo **miami**

photo **new york**

art **los angeles**

artfairs inc.

photo miami

The International Contemporary
Art Fair of Photo-Based Art
Video & New Media

December 4 - 9, 2007
Wynwood Art District

www.artfairsinc.com

SEPTEMBER 1, 2007– AUGUST 31, 2008

THE INTERNATIONAL GUIDE TO ART FAIRS AND ANTIQUES SHOWS

2007/2008 SEASON

Featuring the details on over 100 forthcoming major international events in 33 cities and 18 countries and including more than 70 two-page color presentations of leading shows and 150 color illustrations of artworks and objects to be offered at these events by some of the world's leading art and antiques dealers.

Subscribe now to receive the new annual edition for two years at only $12 per issue. You pay just $24* and you save $12.

*$45 outside the United States

To subscribe by Fax: +1 212 673 9507 or by email: artmediaco@aol.com
For illustration reservations please call +1 212 673 2687 before June 1.

art **on paper**

PRINTS
DRAWINGS
PHOTOGRAPHS
BOOKS
EPHEMERA

The most widely-read, best informed, most controver-
sial contemporay art magazine in the world today.
Flash Art, described as the "reliable barometer of the
Zeitgeist," has become an unrivaled reference point for
artists, critics, art dealers, philosophers, and writers.
Flash Art is there to keep you informed of what is really
happening in the contemporary art world, because
today's news is the history of our time.

Flash Art
The World's Leading Art Magazine

Art Diary 06/07
the world art directory
Those who look for you
look in Art Diary

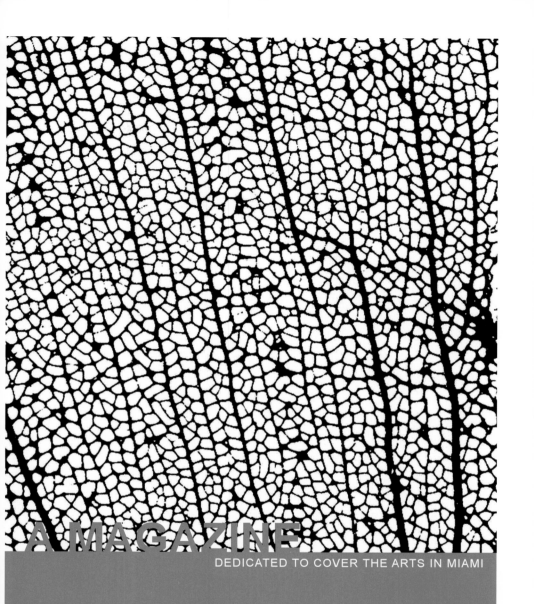

A MAGAZINE

DEDICATED TO COVER THE ARTS IN MIAMI

For more information visit:
www.miamiartguide.com

SUBSCRIBE / ADVERTISE /
(1) 305.573.9530
sales@miamiartguide.com

art is everywhere

MAG

MIAMI ART GUIDE

THE ABSOLUTE GUIDE FOR ART RESOURCES IN MIAMI

PARIS PHOTO

15 -18 NOV. 07

CARROUSEL DU LOUVRE, PARIS

ITALY GUEST OF HONOUR

THE INTERNATIONAL
PHOTOGRAPHY FAIR,
19TH CENTURY, MODERN
& CONTEMPORARY

 Reed Exhibitions

WWW.PARISPHOTO.FR

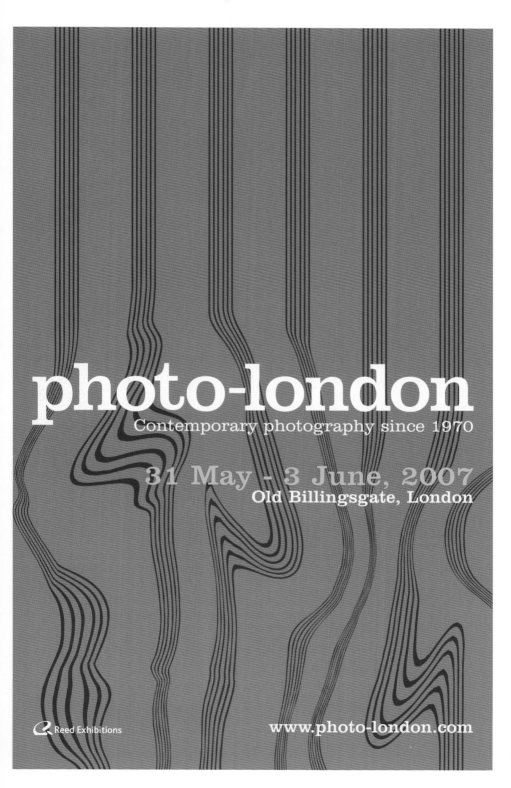

photo-london

Contemporary photography since 1970

31 May - 3 June, 2007
Old Billingsgate, London

Reed Exhibitions

www.photo-london.com

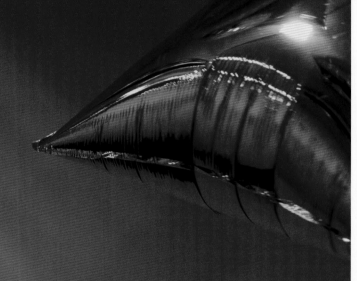

ART APPRECIATION

THE NEW YORKER OFFERS A PORTFOLIO OF MILLIONS OF
READERS COAST-TO-COAST WHO ARE DEVOTED ART BUYERS.

THE NEW YORKER

To reach this audience of art collectors, contact
Kristi Adams at 212.286.5935 or visit newyorkersmallspace.com.

just a click away...

art now online

Andy Warhol
John Baldessari
Salvador Dali
Robert Indiana
Banksy
Julio Larraz
Joan Miro
Georgia O´Keeffe
Pablo Picasso
Auguste Rodin
and more...

Lazarides
Contrasts Gallery
Galeria Pepe Cobo
Kristy Stubbs Gallery
Galerie Barbara Weiss
A arte Studio Invernizzi
Tibor de Nagy Gallery

The concept of art

www.artnowonline.com
info@artnowonline.com

your best art resource

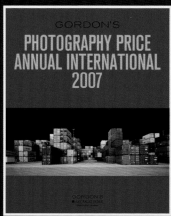

Here is Photography!

www.photography-now.com

The International Online Platform
for Exhibitions, Institutions and Events

Artwork: Bernhard Prinz
Photo: Jens Liebchen

Next Level

ART / PHOTOGRAPHY / IDEAS

EDITION 11 • £12.95

Desire

LORI NIX

"AQUARIUM", 2007, CHROMOGENIC PRINT, 48" x 63"

SHADOWS OF THE CITY

MARCH 8 - APRIL 21, 2007

ILLUSTRATED CATALOG WITH ESSAY BY ROBIN STARBUCK, $20PPD

JENKINS JOHNSON GALLERY

521 West 26th Street • 5th Floor • New York • NY 10001
212.629.0707 • Fax 212.629.4255 • www.jenkinsjohnsongallery.com

EVERYONE HAS STANDARDS...

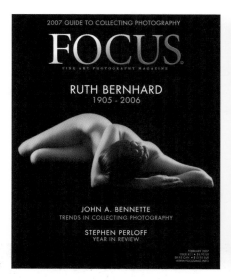

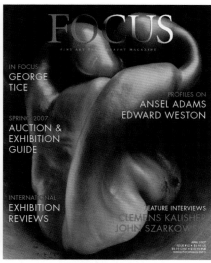

...MAYBE YOURS ARE JUST A LITTLE HIGHER?

Read the latest market news for collecting fine art photography from Stephen Perloff in every issue. Find out the latest trends in collecting photography with John A. Bennette. Find out about upcoming auctions before the general public. Discover new photography books being published each month and read our reviews of the biggest and most important to own. Examine the lives of vintage photographers with Anthony Bannon, the director of the George Eastman House. Go one-on-one with the top photography curators of museums, worldwide. Go in-depth with the most collected photographers today. Recieve detailed reviews of exhibitions from cities all around the world. Preview over 100 photography exhibitions taking place in New York City . . . and so much more. Focus magazine is the only source you need to find out the latest news, trends and information on collecting fine art photography. Subscribe today and receive a free copy of issue 11 or issue 12. And if you subscribe for two years, you will receive the third year absolutely free. Why wait? Subscribe today. www.focusmag.info/aipad.

SUBSCRIBE TO FOCUS MAGAZINE AND
EXPLORE THE NEW STANDARD FOR
FINE ART PHOTOGRAPHY MAGAZINES

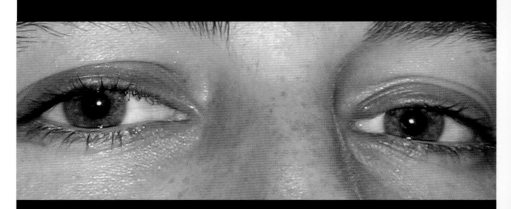

M

The New York Art World®.com

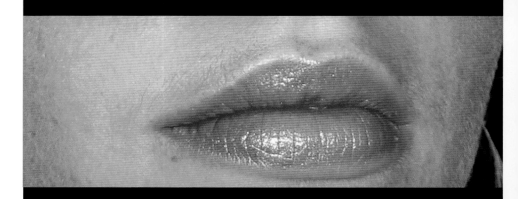

"This is the most comprehensive and thorough guide to New York's art world and galleries I have ever come across. It's all you'll ever need if you are interested in discovering great art in New York."

Ken Johnson
The New York Times

Culture & Travel

THE ULTIMATE MAGAZINE FOR TRAVELERS
WHOSE ENTHUSIASM FOR THE ARTS
KNOWS NO BOUNDARIES.

To subscribe:
www.cultureandtravel.com

PHOTO: RICHARD BARNES

126 Peabody Miami University Oxford, Ohio 45056

p 513/529-8328   f 513/529-9301   www.spenational.org

THE SOCIETY FOR PHOTOGRAPHIC EDUCATION IS THE LONGEST LIVED AND LARGEST ASSOCIATION DEVOTED TO PHOTOGRAPHY AS IT APPLIES TO EDUCATION, PRACTICE AND SCHOLARSHIP.
With a membership that consists primarily of photographic educators on the university level as well as museum professionals, gallery curators, arts administrators, publishers, photo historians, artists, high school teachers, graduate and undergraduate students, SPE provides a unique, international forum for the discussion of photography as a means of creative expression and cultural insight.

Becoming a member of SPE will not only enhance your network of colleagues, but will bring you additional benefits that include:

SPE NATIONAL CONFERENCES
Each spring, SPE hosts a vibrant national conference attended by over 1100 educators, artists, scholars, entrepreneurs and students. The four-day gathering includes lectures, panel discussions and artists' presentations, as well as featured talks by nationally known artists and scholars. Other conference features include an extensive exhibits fair, workshops, portfolio sessions and critiques, gallery receptions and more. Members will receive discounted rates.

SPE PUBLICATIONS
- *exposure.* A finely printed professional publication collected by museums and libraries. Published twice a year, it includes criticism, essays, articles on education as well as book and exhibition reviews.
- *Quarterly newsletters.* An excellent vehicle for information and exchange of SPE business, members' activities, bulletin boards, job listings and more.
- *Membership Directory & Resource Guide.* Used throughout the year by our membership, this publication lists the names and addresses of all SPE officers and members.

AND MORE...
Members also enjoy access to our Fine Print Collectors program as well as automatic membership to a regional chapter and updates through the SPE website.

JOIN US!
Learn more about us by visiting our website, www.spenational.org, or give us a call at 513-529-8328.

cover image: Myra Greene, Untitled, 2006, Ambrotype,
3 x 4 inches, courtesy of the artist

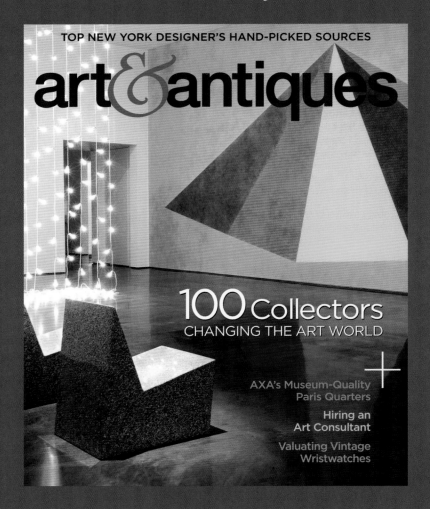

Chris Beetles Gallery, England presents

SNOWDON

IN NEW YORK

The first selling exhibition of Snowdon's photography in America

March 1 – April 21, 2007

Images available to view online at www.chrisbeetles.com
Full colour illustrated catalogue available

Godel & Co. Fine Art, 39A East 72nd Street, New York, NY
(212) 288 7272   info@godelfineart.com   www.chrisbeetles.com

IMAGO

**The only magazine about contemporary photography
of Central and Eastern Europe published in English.**

Three portfolios of contemporary photographers are included in each issue along
with essays on current issues, texts from history of photography, interviews with critics
and artists, presentations of photo-galleries and photo-academies, reviews of books,
exhibitions, magazines and events as well as schedules of the most important photo-
-galleries in Central and Eastern Europe. IMAGO is published twice a year.

Publisher: FOTOFO, Prepoštská 4, P.O. Box 290, 814 99 Bratislava, Slovakia
www.sedf.sk, lucia.lendelova@gmail.com

Mark Raidpere, still from: Andrey/Andris, 2006 (detail)

STARR OCKENGA

PRESENCE

SOME DETAILS FROM A GARDEN

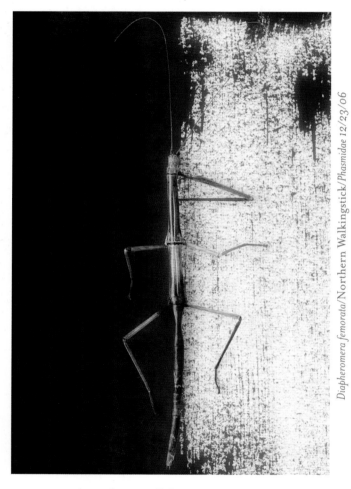

Diapheromera femorata/Northern Walkingstick/Phasmidae 12/23/06

April 12 - May 19, 2007

The Suchman-Bart-Metheny Gallery

547 W 27th St, NY, NY 10001, 5th fl 212.695.0021 / www.triagallerynyc.com
info@triagallerynyc.com / Hours: Wed. - Sat. 11:00 am - 6:00 pm

MONROE GALLERY

of photography

Specializing in classic black and white photography,
with an emphasis on humanist and photojournalist imagery.

Oil Field worker, Freer, Texas, 1937 Carl Mydans ©Time Inc

Black Muslim leader Malcolm X photographing Cassius Clay surrounded by jubilant fans after he
beat Sonny Liston for the heavyweight championship of the world, Miami, March, 1964 Bob Gomel

FaridaWorksHere.com

ANNUAL ART AUCTION
PORTRAITS & POLAROIDS
MONDAY APRIL.23.2007

INCLUDES WORKS BY:
CHUCK CLOSE
TODD EBERLE
ADAM FUSS
NAN GOLDIN
ERWIN OLAF
CATHERINE OPIE
ANDRES SERRANO
NEIL WINOKUR
& MORE

ALL PROCEEDS BENEFIT FREE ARTS NYC A NON-PROFIT ORGANIZATION
PROVIDING ART MENTORS TO AT-RISK CHILDREN AND FAMILIES.

FOR MORE INFORMATION AND TO PREVIEW IMAGES WWW.FREEARTSNYC.ORG

 Free Arts NYC
Art Heals. Mentoring Works.
1431 BROADWAY 7TH FLOOR NY NY 10018 212.974.9092

IMAGE AND CULTURE

Fernando Ortega. *Untitled*, 2006. Videostill. Courtesy of Kurimanzutto Gallery, Mexico City

w w w . e x i t m e d i a . n e t

Photography & Contemporary Art
Quarterly Magazine
Bilingual Edition: English / Spanish
Thematic · Essays · Interviews · Portfolios

Published by Rosa Olivares & Associates
San Marcelo, 30 · E28017 MADRID · SPAIN
Tel. +34 914 049 740 · Fax +34 913 260 012
exit@exitmedia.net · www.exitmedia.net

A-57

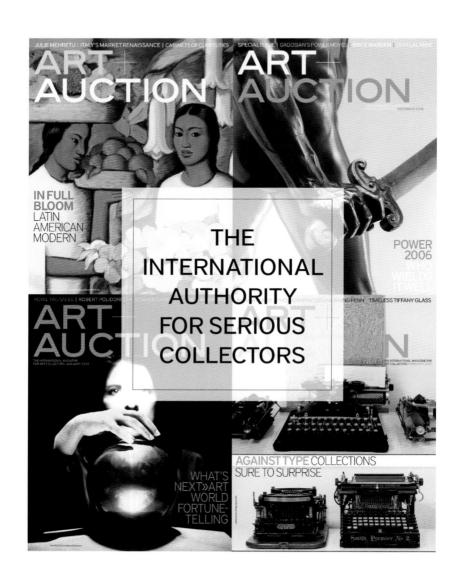

THE
INTERNATIONAL
AUTHORITY
FOR SERIOUS
COLLECTORS

SUBSCRIBE:
WWW.ARTINFO.COM
AMERICAS +1 800 777 8718 INTERNATIONAL +44 (0) 870 428 7969

Goldman, Sachs & Co. is proud to support
A.C.E. for the Homeless
and the AIPAD's Photography Show.

Style

MONTE CARLO

Photograph by Amedeo M.Turello

TAKE A RIDE ON THE BEAST OF FASHION

at@stylemontecarlo.com - www.stylemontecarlo.com

Distributed worldwide by COMAG, a company within the Condé Nast Group and through
selected retailers by LMPI Canada and Svenska Interpress.

© Richard J. Linke

© Susana Reisman

THE CENTER FOR PHOTOGRAPHY AT WOODSTOCK

exhibitions | workshops | lectures
photography quarterly magazine
residencies | fellowship | library
permanent print collection
artist services | more

59 TINKER STREET
WOODSTOCK
NEW YORK 12498
T. 845 679 9957
WWW.CPW.ORG

TEPPER TAKAYAMA
FINE ARTS

YOSHI ABE	HIROMITSU MORIMOTO	KUNIHIRO SHINOHARA
LAURENT ELIE BADESSI	DAIDO MORIYAMA	VILMA SLOMP
RENAN CEPEDA	DAI NAKAMURA	YASU SUZUKA
ANDREW FLADEBOE	ROGERIO REIS	EVANDRO TEIXEIRA
HELEN K. GARBER	PAOLO ROSSELLI	SHOMEI TOMATSU
ANNA BELLA GEIGER	EIICHIRO SAKATA	HIROMI TSUCHIDA
CRISTIANO MASCARO	PAVLOS SATOGLOU	CASSIO VASCONCELLOS
MILAN	TOSHIO SHIBATA	JANEZ VLACHY
MILTON MONTENEGRO	QUENTIN SHIH	ROBERT WELSH
EDGAR MORENO	EDUARDO SIMOES	WONG HOY CHEONG

20 Park Plaza, Suite 600 ■ Boston, MA 02116 ■ tel 617-542-0557 ■ fax 617-542-0607
www.teppertakayamafinearts.com ■ info@teppertakayamafinearts.com

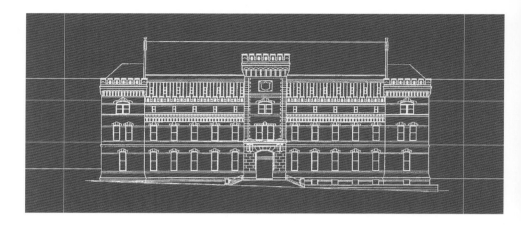

The Seventh Regiment Armory Conservancy, Inc.

About the Conservancy

The Conservancy's mission is to restore and revitalize the Park Avenue Armory, one of New York's most important historic structures, and weave it back into the social and cultural fabric of the city. Built in the late 1880s, the building contains the 55,000-square foot Drill Hall and the country's most intact collection of American Aesthetic Movement interiors, representing the work of Louis Comfort Tiffany, Stanford White, the Herter Brothers, and other important designers of the period. The revitalized Armory will be a major achievement for historic restoration, giving a truly significant landmark new life as a unique center for culture, celebration, and learning.

Find Out More

For more information about the Conservancy and its plans, to find out how you can help, or to arrange a tour of the Armory's hidden treasures, please call 212-616-3937, or visit our website at www.armoryonpark.org.

CROSS-REFERENCE OF PHOTOGRAPHERS REPRESENTED BY AIPAD MEMBERS

Photographers (in bold type) are listed alphabetically. Information concerning the AIPAD members following each photographer's name can be found in the "Illustrated Catalogue Entries" listed alphabetically in the preceding pages.

A

Mario A   Esther Woerdehoff

Slim Aarons   Staley+Wise, Candace Dwan

Stanko Abadzic   John Cleary, Contemporary / Vintage Works

James Abbe   Richard T. Rosenthal

Berenice Abbott   Lee Marks, Commerce Graphics, Alan Klotz, Robert Mann, Peter Fetterman, Michael Shapiro, Joel Soroka, Contemporary / Vintage Works, Paul M. Hertzmann, Zur Stockeregg, Wach Gallery, William L. Schaeffer, Charles Schwartz, Henry Feldstein, Keith de Lellis, G. Gibson Gallery, Halsted Gallery, Scott Nichols, Joseph Bellows, Robert Klein, Barry Singer, Bonni Benrubi, HackelBury, Howard Greenberg, Gallery 19/21, Scheinbaum & Russek, Lee Gallery, Richard Moore, Zabriskie Gallery, Richard T. Rosenthal, Ezra Mack, Robert Miller

Jun Abe   Picture Photo Space

Sam Abell   Kathleen Ewing

Laurence Aberhart   McNamara Gallery

Vito Acconci   Deborah Bell

Hector Acebes   G. Gibson Gallery

Ansel Adams   Andrew Smith, Etherton Gallery, Robert Mann, Halsted Gallery, Paul M. Hertzmann, Jan Kesner, Robert Koch, Michael Shapiro, Alan Klotz, Robert Klein, Byron McMahon, Weston Gallery, Zur Stockeregg, Scheinbaum & Russek, Henry Feldstein, Joseph Bellows, Charles A. Hartman, Scott Nichols, Barry Singer, G. Gibson Gallery, A Gallery, Michael Dawson, Richard Moore, William L. Schaeffer, Wach Gallery

Mark Adams   McNamara Gallery

Robert Adams   Fraenkel Gallery

Shelby Lee Adams   Catherine Edelman, Stephen Bulger, Fahey/Klein

Robert Adamson   Lee Gallery

Ruven Afanador   Throckmorton Fine Art

African-American Vernacular   TARTT/washington

Olympe Aguado   Hans P. Kraus, Jr., michèle chomette

Judith Ahern   Byron McMahon

Josef Albers   Deborah Bell

Laure Albin-Guillot   Contemporary / Vintage Works, Joel Soroka, Charles A. Hartman, A Gallery, Joseph Bellows, Zabriskie Gallery, Paul M. Hertzmann

John Albok   Photographs Do Not Bend

Jose Alemany   Henry Feldstein, Richard T. Rosenthal

Jesse Alexander   Halsted Gallery, Peter Fetterman, Photographs Do Not Bend, Robert Klein, Staley+Wise

Mario Algaze   Throckmorton Fine Art

Fratelli Alinari   William L. Schaeffer, Alan Klotz

Lyle Allan   Wach Gallery

William Albert Allard   David Gallery

Albert Arthur Allen   Etherton Gallery, Henry Feldstein, Richard T. Rosenthal

Stuart Allen   Photographs Do Not Bend

David Allison   Kathleen Ewing

Jocelyne Alloucherie   Françoise Paviot

Joan Almond   Halsted Gallery

Juan Carlos Alom   Throckmorton Fine Art

Merry Alpern   Bonni Benrubi

Max Alpert   Nailya Alexander

Dag Alveng   Deborah Bell

Ambrotypes   Ezra Mack, Wach Gallery

American Vernacular   Gary Edwards

Fiona Amundsen   McNamara Gallery

Henry Clay Anderson   Steven Kasher

Paul L. Anderson   Richard T. Rosenthal

Anderson & Low   David Gallery, Kathleen Ewing, Jackson Fine Art

Erich Angenendt   Gitterman Gallery

Thomas Annan   Ken & Jenny Jacobson

Roswell Angier   Gitterman Gallery

Allen Appel   Kathleen Ewing

Dieter Appelt   Pace/MacGill, Françoise Paviot, Hyperion Press, Kicken Berlin

Nobuyoshi Araki   Picture Photo Space, Michael Hoppen, Photology

Diane Arbus   Robert Mann, Fraenkel Gallery, Jan Kesner, Robert Klein, Picture Photo Space, Stephen Cohen, Howard Greenberg, Lee Marks, G. Gibson Gallery, HackelBury, Michael Hoppen, Edwynn Houk, RoseGallery, Esther Woerdehoff, Robert Miller, Laurence Miller, Silverstein Photography

Fred Archer   Joseph Bellows

Tom Archibald   Etherton Gallery

Dick Arentz   Etherton Gallery, Stephen Bulger, Johannes Faber

Laura Adams Armer   Richard Moore

Bill Armstrong   Wm. Floyd

Frank Armstrong   Stephen L. Clark

Eve Arnold   David Gallery, Paul M. Hertzmann

Steven Arnold   Wessel+O'Connor

Ursula Arnold   argus-fotokunst

Kiitchi Asano   Eric Franck, Stephen Cohen, Scott Nichols

Eugène Atget   Charles Isaacs, Lee Marks, Fraenkel Gallery, Hyperion Press, Janet Lehr, Robert Koch, Alan Klotz, Robert Klein, Lee Gallery, Paul M. Hertzmann, Zur Stockeregg, Françoise Paviot, Jan Kesner, Hans P. Kraus, Jr., Gitterman Gallery, Barry Singer, Edwynn Houk, Contemporary / Vintage Works, Peter Fetterman, Gallery 19/21, Weston Gallery, Galerie 1900/2000, Serge Plantureux, Zabriskie Gallery, Robert Hershkowitz, Deborah Bell, William L. Schaeffer, Silverstein Photography, Robert Miller

Athletic Model Guild   Wessel+O'Connor

Anna Atkins   Hans P. Kraus, Jr., Ezra Mack

Charles Aubry   Charles Isaacs

Louis Aubry   Hans P. Kraus, Jr., Gitterman Gallery

Ellen Auerbach   Robert Mann

Narelle Autio   Ariel Meyerowitz

Richard Avedon   Zur Stockeregg, Keith de Lellis, Fraenkel Gallery, Byron McMahon, Michael Hoppen, Steven Kasher, Photology

Sid Avery   Staley+Wise, David Gallery

Ragnar Axelsson   argus-fotokunst

B

Kurt Baasch   Joseph Bellows

Jessica Backhaus   Yancey Richardson

Morley Baer   Lee Marks

Julia Baier   Photo ART

David Bailey   Fahey/Klein

Oscar Bailey   Joseph Bellows

Patrick Bailly-Maitre-Grand   Baudoin Lebon

Edouard Denis Baldus   Charles Isaacs, Robert Koch, michèle chomette, Gallery 19/21, Janet Lehr, Alan Klotz, Robert Klein, Gallery, William L. Schaeffer, Hans P. Kraus, Jr., Lee Gallery, Françoise Paviot, Contemporary / Vintage Works, TARTT/washington, Weston Gallery, Daniel Blau, Gitterman Gallery, Zabriskie Gallery, Richard T. Rosenthal, Robert Hershkowitz, Ezra Mack, Serge Plantureux

José Manuel Ballester   Charles Cowles

Roger Ballen   Michael Hoppen, Jackson Fine Art, Catherine Edelman, Robert Klein, Fahey/Klein

Lewis Baltz   Hyperion Press, Yancey Richardson, gallery luisotti, Contemporary / Vintage Works

John Banasiak   Joseph Bellows

Pavel Banka   Alan Klotz

Bruno Barbey   Barry Singer, Steven Kasher

Gian Paolo Barbieri   Photology

Cara Barer   Barry Singer

Tom Baril   Catherine Edelman, Hyperion Press, Robert Koch, Robert Klein, Joel Soroka

Jeff Bark   Michael Hoppen

George Barker   TARTT/washington

George Barnard   William L. Schaeffer, Lee Gallery

Bruce Barnbaum   Kathleen Ewing, A Gallery

Tina Barney   Janet Borden

Wayne Barrar   McNamara Gallery

Greg Barrett   Josef Lebovic

Geraldo de Barros   Eric Franck

Reenie Barrow   Robert Burge

Ralph Bartholomew   Keith de Lellis

Adam Bartos   RoseGallery, Yossi Milo

Josef Bartuska   Charles A. Hartman, Czech Center

Peter Basch   Staley+Wise

Lilian Bassmann   Michael Hoppen, Staley+Wise, Peter Fetterman

John Batho   Zabriskie Gallery

Elmer Batters   Henry Feldstein

Bauhaus   Priska Pasquer, michèle chomette, Kicken Berlin

Bayard   Hans P. Kraus, Jr.

Herbert Bayer   Joel Soroka

Janet Bayly   McNamara Gallery

Robert W. Bazemore, Jr.   Kathleen Ewing

Gustave de Beaucorps   Robert Hershkowitz

Beahan & McPhee   RoseGallery

Virginia Beahan   Joseph Bellows

Mark Beard   John Stevenson

Peter Beard   Fahey/Klein, Michael Hoppen, A Gallery

Felice Beato   Robert Koch, Alan Klotz, Robert Klein, Charles Schwartz, Ken & Jenny Jacobson, TARTT/washington, Zabriskie Gallery

Cecil Beaton   Staley+Wise, Henry Feldstein, Keith de Lellis, Daniel Blau, Johannes Faber, Zabriskie Gallery, Richard T. Rosenthal, Robert Miller

E. Bechard   Ken & Jenny Jacobson

Bernd & Hilla Becher   Fraenkel Gallery, Kicken Berlin

Carol Beckwith & Angela Fisher   Staley+Wise

Jeffrey Becom   Lee Marks, Yancey Richardson, John Cleary, Barry Singer, Weston Gallery

Henri Becquerel   Robert Hershkowitz

Valerie Bélin   Michael Hoppen

William Bell   Etherton Gallery, William L. Schaeffer

Hans Bellmer   Hyperion Press, Galerie 1900/2000

E. J. Bellocq   Fraenkel Gallery, Picture Photo Space, Janet Borden

Ernest Benecke   Gary Edwards

Harry Benson   Staley+Wise, David Gallery

Wilson A. Bentley   HASTED HUNT

Grant Beran   McNamara Gallery

Steven Berardelli   G. Gibson Gallery

Sibylle Bergemann   argus-fotokunst

Wout Berger   Bonni Benrubi

Phil Bergerson   Stephen Bulger

Ladislav Emil Berka   Czech Center

Michael Berman   Scheinbaum & Russek, Etherton Gallery, Stephen L. Clark

Zeke Berman   Laurence Miller

Mathieu Bernard-Reymond   Baudoin Lebon

Ruth Bernhard   John Cleary, Peter Fetterman, Michael Shapiro, Scott Nichols, Paul M. Hertzmann, Henry Feldstein, Halsted Gallery, John Stevenson, G. Gibson Gallery, Michael Dawson, Charles A. Hartman

Per Berntsen   Deborah Bell

Ian Berry   Steven Kasher

Paul Berthier   Daniel Blau, Contemporary / Vintage Works

Gaston Bertin   Galerie 1900/2000

John Bertolino   Paul M. Hertzmann

Auguste Bertsch   Contemporary / Vintage Works

Robert Besanko   Josef Lebovic

Joseph Beuys   Scheinbaum & Russek

Peter Bialobrzeski   Laurence Miller

Lynn Bianchi   Joel Soroka

Robert Bianchi   Joel Soroka

Tom Bianchi   Throckmorton Fine Art

Jayne Hinds Bidaut   Joseph Bellows

Ilse Bing   Zur Stockeregg, Henry Feldstein, Paul M. Hertzmann, Joel Soroka, Lee Gallery, Contemporary / Vintage Works, Charles A. Hartman, Edwynn Houk, Michael Shapiro, Zabriskie Gallery, Barry Singer, Silverstein Photography

Jeanne Birdsall   Kathleen Ewing

Werner Bischof   Charles A. Hartman, Steven Kasher

Bisson-Frères   Lee Gallery, Ken & Jenny Jacobson, Hans P. Kraus, Jr., Alan Klotz, Gallery 19/21, Contemporary / Vintage Works, Zabriskie Gallery

James Wallace Black   William L. Schaeffer

Peter Black   McNamara Gallery

Gary Blackman   McNamara Gallery

Julie Blackmon   G. Gibson Gallery, Catherine Edelman

Tom Blake   Ariel Meyerowitz

Blanc and Demilly   Joel Soroka, Gallery 19/21, Galerie 1900/2000

Nealy Blau   G. Gibson Gallery

Lucienne Bloch   Throckmorton Fine Art

Debra Bloomfield   Etherton Gallery, Robert Koch

Karl Blossfeldt   Lee Marks, Kicken Berlin, Lisa Sette

Donald Blumberg   Jan Kesner

Bernard and Anna Blume   Françoise Paviot, Kicken Berlin

Erwin Blumenfeld   Deborah Bell, Paul M. Hertzmann, Fahey/Klein, Joel Soroka, Priska Pasquer, Zabriskie Gallery

A. Aubrey Bodine   Kathleen Ewing, Wm. Floyd, Henry Feldstein, Richard T. Rosenthal

Marco Bohr   Stephen Bulger

J-A Boiffard   Galerie 1900/2000

Ave Bonar   Stephen L. Clark

Felix Bonfils   Ken & Jenny Jacobson, Alan Klotz, Gary Edwards

Benedetta Bonichi   Keith de Lellis

Lou Bonin-Tchimoukoff   Johannes Faber

Rudolf Bonvie   Priska Pasquer

Alvin Booth   Fahey/Klein, Throckmorton Fine Art, Robert Klein

Christian Borchert   argus-fotokunst

Andrew Bordwin   Julie Saul

Phil Borges   Kathleen Ewing

Polly Borland   Michael Hoppen

Lev Borodulin   Nailya Alexander

Andrew Borowiec   Lee Marks

Cecil Bostock   Josef Lebovic

Rhondda Bosworth   McNamara Gallery

Machiel Botman   Gitterman Gallery

Corinne May Botz   HEMPHILL

Edouard Boubat   Hyperion Press, Candace Dwan, Contemporary / Vintage Works, Esther Woerdehoff, Gallery 19/21, Zabriskie Gallery, Scheinbaum & Russek

Pierre Boucher   Gitterman Gallery, Zabriskie Gallery

Alice Boughton   Richard T. Rosenthal

Alexandra Boulat   HASTED HUNT

Guy Bourdin   Françoise Paviot, Michael Hoppen

France Bourély   Wm. Floyd

Margaret Bourke-White   John Cleary, Lee Gallery, Michael Shapiro, Wach Gallery, Zur Stockeregg, William L. Schaeffer, Paul M. Hertzmann, Keith de Lellis, Alan Klotz, Candace Dwan, Charles Schwartz, David Gallery, Barry Singer, Daniel Blau, Edwynn Houk, David Gallery

Samuel Bourne   Gary Edwards, Ken & Jenny Jacobson, Alan Klotz, TARTT/washington, Joseph Bellows, Robert Hershkowitz

Marcel Bovis   Contemporary / Vintage Works, Zabriskie Gallery

Gilbert Boyer   michèle chomette

Jack Bradley   Wm. Floyd

Mathew Brady   Wach Gallery, Janet Lehr

Stuart M. Brafman   Kathleen Ewing

Bragaglia Brothers   Hyperion Press

Stern J. Bramson   Paul Kopeikin

Constantin Brancusi   Zur Stockeregg, Françoise Paviot, Paul M. Hertzmann, Gitterman Gallery, Ezra Mack, Silverstein Photography

Bill Brandt   Stephen Daiter, Paul M. Hertzmann, Michael Hoppen, Zur Stockeregg, Lee Gallery, Halsted Gallery, Barry Singer, Henry Feldstein, Hyperion Press, Charles Isaacs, Charles A. Hartman, John Cleary, Weston Gallery, Deborah Bell, William L. Schaeffer, Fahey/Klein, Gitterman Gallery, Edwynn Houk, Robert Koch, Scheinbaum & Russek, Silverstein Photography, Wach Gallery

Nick Brandt   Stephen Cohen, Byron McMahon, Staley+Wise

Brassaï   Robert Koch, Michael Hoppen, Alan Klotz, Robert Klein, Wach Gallery, Zur Stockeregg, Henry Feldstein, Fahey/Klein, Paul M. Hertzmann, Françoise Paviot, Candace Dwan, Contemporary / Vintage Works, Gallery 19/21, Bonni Benrubi, Galerie 1900/2000, Edwynn Houk, Richard Moore, Zabriskie Gallery, Joel Soroka, Silverstein Photography, Robert Miller

Adolphe Braun   Ken & Jenny Jacobson, Halsted Gallery, Alan Klotz, Janet Lehr, Contemporary / Vintage Works, Lee Gallery, William L. Schaeffer

Lola Alvarez Bravo   Photographs Do Not Bend, Throckmorton Fine Art

Manuel Alvarez Bravo   John Cleary, Henry Feldstein, RoseGallery, Paul M. Hertzmann, Hyperion Press, William L. Schaeffer, Scheinbaum & Russek, Fahey/Klein, Etherton Gallery, Andrew Smith, Throckmorton Fine Art, Zur Stockeregg, Charles Schwartz, G. Gibson Gallery, Edwynn Houk, Halsted Gallery, Contemporary / Vintage Works, Jan Kesner

Kate Breakey   Etherton Gallery, Stephen L. Clark

Hugo Brehme   Henry Feldstein, Throckmorton Fine Art

Josef Breitenbach   Stephen Daiter, Paul M. Hertzmann

Frédéric Brenner   Howard Greenberg

Frank Breuer   gallery luisotti

Marilyn Bridges   David Gallery

Rev. George Bridges   Robert Hershkowitz

Anne Brigman   Scott Nichols, Joseph Bellows, Paul M. Hertzmann, Barry Singer, Lee Gallery, Jan Kesner, Richard Moore, William L. Schaeffer

Alexandre Brignoli   Ken & Jenny Jacobson

Denis Brihat   Candace Dwan

Abel Briquet   Throckmorton Fine Art

Horace Bristol   Stephen Cohen, Michael Shapiro, Michael Dawson, Robert Miller

Linda Broadfoot   John Stevenson

Steven Brock   Michael Shapiro

Joachim Brohm   gallery luisotti

Jindrich Brok   Czech Center

Kaucyila Brooke   Michael Dawson

Reva Brooks   Stephen Bulger

Jeff Brouws   Robert Mann, Robert Koch, Robert Klein

Anthony Browell   Josef Lebovic

Peter Brown   Stephen Cohen, Stephen L. Clark

Zoe Lowenthal Brown Paul M. Hertzmann

Bruce of L. A. Scott Nichols, Throckmorton Fine Art, Wessel+O'Connor

Anton Bruehl Throckmorton Fine Art

Francis Bruguiere Paul M. Hertzmann

Blanca Casas Brullet Françoise Paviot

Guiseppe Bruno Keith de Lellis

Esther Bubley Kathleen Ewing, Deborah Bell, Keith de Lellis, Howard Greenberg, Michael Shapiro

Wiliam G. Buckle Josef Lebovic

Christopher Bucklow Gallery

Vladimir Jindrich Bufka Czech Center

Clarence Sinclair Bull Staley + Wise, Richard T. Rosenthal

Wynn Bullock Scott Nichols, Wach Gallery, Richard Moore, Scheinbaum & Russek, Henry Feldstein, Paul M. Hertzmann, Barry Singer, Etherton Gallery, Stephen Daiter, Joseph Bellows, Weston Gallery, G. Gibson Gallery, William L. Schaeffer

Bill Burke Howard Greenberg

Christopher Burkett Kathleen Ewing, Etherton Gallery

Dan Burkholder John Cleary

Robert Burley Stephen Bulger

Rene Burri Zur Stockeregg, Esther Woerdehoff argus-fotokunst

Larry Burrows Laurence Miller

Nancy Burson Jan Kesner, michèle chomette

Andrew Bush Julie Saul

Linda Butler G. Gibson Gallery, Weston Gallery

Wendy Burton Lee Marks

Edward Burtynsky Robert Koch, Charles Cowles

David Byrne Pace/MacGill

C

Debbie Fleming Caffery Robert Koch, Etherton Gallery, Gitterman Gallery, Joseph Bellows, G. Gibson Gallery

Nicholas Caire Josef Lebovic

Caithness & Bembridge Lee Marks

Richard Caldicott Ariel Meyerowitz

Colby Caldwell Nailya Alexander, HEMPHILL

Larry Calkins G. Gibson Gallery

Harry Callahan Etherton Gallery, Fraenkel Gallery, Jackson Fine Art, Pace/MacGill, Paul M. Hertzmann, Scheinbaum & Russek, Stephen Daiter, Robert Klein, Henry Feldstein, Lee Marks, Alan Klotz, Deborah Bell, Scott Nichols, Charles A. Hartman, William L. Schaeffer, HackelBury, Gitterman Gallery, TARTT/washington, Zabriskie Gallery, Contemporary / Vintage Works, Silverstein Photography, Jan Kesner

Dennis Callwood Charles Isaacs

Camera Notes Picture Photo Space

Camera Work William L. Schaeffer, Etherton Gallery, Lee Marks, Joseph Bellows, Alan Klotz, Picture Photo Space, John Cleary, Photo Space, Charles A.Hartman, Scheinbaum & Russek, John Stevenson, G. Gibson Gallery, Lee Gallery, Wach Gallery

Joe Cameron Kathleen Ewing

Julia Margaret Cameron Charles Isaacs, Hans P. Kraus, Jr., Janet Lehr, Robert Koch, Alan Klotz, Robert Klein, Contemporary / Vintage Works, Halsted Gallery, Weston Gallery, Robert Hershkowitz

Murray Cammick McNamara Gallery

Elaine Campaner McNamara Gallery

Joyce Campbell McNamara Gallery

Maria Magdalena Campos-Pons Julie Saul

Caneva Hans P. Kraus, Jr., Serge Plantureux

Augusto Cantamessa Keith de Lellis

Cornell Capa Peter Fetterman Steven Kasher

Robert Capa Lee Marks, Howard Greenberg, Peter Fetterman, TARTT/washington, Steven Kasher

Lana Caplan John Stevenson

Paul Caponigro Etherton Gallery, Peter Fetterman, Scott Nichols, Andrew Smith, Joseph Bellows, Scheinbaum & Russek, Charles A. Hartman

Samuel Capuano Richard T. Rosenthal

Marty Carden John Cleary

Manuel Carillo Scheinbaum & Russek

Brigitte Carnochan John Stevenson, Peter Fetterman

Carpenter Richard T. Rosenthal

Bertrand Carriere Stephen Bulger

Mario Carrieri Keith de Lellis

Lewis Carroll Charles Isaacs, Robert Koch, Hans P. Kraus, Jr., Contemporary / Vintage Works, Robert Hershkowitz

Geoff Carter Wm. Floyd

Jeff Carter Byron McMahon

Keith Carter Catherine Edelman, Photographs Do Not Bend, Stephen L. Clark, Etherton Gallery, G. Gibson Gallery, Johannes Faber, Howard Greenberg

William Carter Wach Gallery

Cartes-de-visite William L. Schaeffer

Henri Cartier-Bresson John Cleary, Jackson Fine Art, Peter Fetterman, Serge Plantureux, Fahey/Klein, Zur Stockeregg, Robert Koch, Yancey Richardson, Michael Shapiro, Scheinbaum & Russek, Scott Nichols, Andrew Smith, Keith de Lellis, HackelBury, Henry Feldstein, Paul M. Hertzmann, Robert Klein, Joel Soroka, Howard Greenberg, Michael Hoppen, Johannes Faber, Bonni Benrubi, Halsted Gallery, Françoise Paviot, Stephen Daiter, Eric Franck, Byron McMahon, G. Gibson Gallery, A Gallery, Photology, Contemporary / Vintage Works, Galerie 1900/2000, Edwynn Houk, Throckmorton Fine Art, Esther Woerdehoff, Gallery 19/21, Charles Schwartz, Silverstein Photography

Elinor Carucci Edwynn Houk

Martha Casanave Gallery 19/21, John Stevenson

Agustin Victor Casasola Throckmorton Fine Art

Oraien E. Catledge Jackson Fine Art

Tony Catany John Stevenson

Roger Catherineau Gitterman Gallery

Jack Cato Josef Lebovic

Mario Cattaneo Keith de Lellis

Ben Cauchi McNamara Gallery

Harold Cazneaux Josef Lebovic

Loris Cecchini Photology

Martin Chambi Throckmorton Fine Art

Chien-Chi Chang Julie Saul

Chan Chao Yancey Richardson, Paul Kopeikin

Song Chao Baudoin Lebon

Arthur D. Chapman Joseph Bellows

Rick Chapman Paul Kopeikin,

Walter Chappell Scheinbaum & Russek, Charles A. Hartman

Simon Chaput Howard Greenberg

Desire Charnay Contemporary / Vintage Works, Charles Isaacs, Robert Hershkowitz

Roz Chast Julie Saul

G.E. Chauffourier Ken & Jenny Jacobson

Frank Chauvassaignes Charles Isaacs

Michal Chelbin Fahey/Klein

Andrey Chezhin Nailya Alexander

Tseng Kwong Chi Robert Klein, Stephen Cohen

Carl Chiarenza Stephen Cohen, Robert Klein

China Alan Klotz

Benjamen Chinn Paul M. Hertzmann, Scott Nichols

Ron Church Scott Nichols

William Christenberry Pace/MacGill, Wm. Floyd, TARTT/washington, G. Gibson Gallery, HEMPHILL, Jackson Fine Art

Joy Christiansen Photographs Do Not Bend

Olivier Christinat Picture Photo Space

Christo Ezra Mack

Mark Citret Halsted Gallery, Michael Shapiro, Weston Gallery

Civil Rights Movement Steven Kasher

Civil War Photographs Richard T. Rosenthal, Charles Isaacs

Arnaud Claass michèle chomette

Clark & Pougnaud Catherine Edelman, Baudoin Lebon

Douglas Clark Stephen Bulger

Ed Clark Keith de Lellis

Fiona Clark McNamara Gallery

Larry Clark Picture Photo Space, John Cleary, Stephen Cohen, Henry Feldstein, Jan Kesner

William Claxton Fahey/Klein, Michael Hoppen, Steven Kasher

Alain Gerard Clement Lisa Sette

Krass Clement argus-fotokunst

Lucien Clergue John Stevenson, Throckmorton Fine Art

Charles Clifford Contemporary / Vintage Works, Robert Hershkowitz

William Clift Scheinbaum & Russek, Charles A. Hartman

Chuck Close Pace/MacGill, Fraenkel Gallery

Jody Cobb David Gallery

Alvin Langdon Coburn Janet Lehr, Richard Moore, William L. Schaeffer, Wach Gallery, Lee Gallery, Paul M. Hertzmann, Hans P. Kraus, Jr., Joseph Bellows, Halsted Gallery, Ezra Mack, Eric Franck

Robert Coburn Fahey/Klein

Elaine Lustig Cohen Julie Saul

John Cohen Deborah Bell, Charles A. Hartman

Lynne Cohen HASTED HUNT

Mark Cohen Zabriskie Gallery, Robert Klein, RoseGallery

J. Walter Collinge Joseph Bellows

Ken Collins Gitterman Gallery

Richard Collins McNamara Gallery

Joan Colom Laurence Miller

Larry Colwell Barry Singer, Joseph Bellows

Scott Conarroe Stephen Bulger

Jeffrey Conley John Cleary

Kelli Connell Yossi Milo, Weinstein Gallery

Will Connell Michael Dawson, Richard Moore

Bruce Connew McNamara Gallery

Gregory Conniff Candace Dwan

Linda Connor Etherton Gallery, Yancey Richardson, G. Gibson Gallery, Joseph Bellows

Dmitri Constantine Gary Edwards

Diane Cook Kathleen Ewing

Mariana Cook Lee Marks

Rod Cook Stephen Daiter, Joel Soroka

Jim Cooke Yancey Richardson

Horacio Coppola argus-fotokunst

Livia Corona Stephen Cohen

Camille Corot Ezra Mack, Serge Plantureux

Carlotta Corpron Photographs Do Not Bend, Alan Klotz, Charles A. Hartman

Giacomo Costa Photology

Harold Holiday Costain Keith de Lellis

Gordon Coster Keith de Lellis

Olive Cotton Josef Lebovic, Byron McMahon

Christian Courreges Baudoin Lebon

Stephane Couturier Laurence Miller

René Cox Robert Miller

Charles Cramer John Cleary

Konrad Cramer Zabriskie Gallery

Barbara Crane Stephen Daiter, Françoise Paviot

Christian Cravo Throckmorton Fine Art

Ralston Crawford Zabriskie Gallery, Richard T. Rosenthal

Fred Cray Janet Borden

Ted Croner Howard Greenberg, HackelBury

Michael Crouser John Stevenson

Lisa Crowley McNamara Gallery

Valdir Cruz Throckmorton Fine Art

Libby Cullen Kathleen Ewing

Robert Cumming Janet Borden

Rebecca Cummins Alan Klotz

Imogen Cunningham Howard Greenberg, Paul M. Hertzmann, Jan Kesner, Scott Nichols, Michael Shapiro, Wach Gallery, John Stevenson, Robert Koch, G. Gibson Gallery, Zur Stockeregg, Charles Isaacs, Joseph Bellows, Charles A. Hartman, Fay Gold, Weston Gallery, Halsted Gallery, Edwynn Houk, Richard Moore, Silverstein Photography, gallery luisotti

Francis Edmund Currey William L. Schaeffer

Asahel Curtis Richard T. Rosenthal

Edward S. Curtis Andrew Smith, Etherton Gallery, Robert Koch, Halsted Gallery, Robert Klein, William L. Schaeffer, Scott Nichols, Janet Lehr, Alan Klotz, Photographs Do Not Bend, Michael Dawson, A Gallery, Zabriskie Gallery, Richard T. Rosenthal, Wach Gallery

Eugène Cuvelier Lee Gallery, Hans P. Kraus, Jr., Contemporary / Vintage Works, William L. Schaeffer, michèle chomette, Weston Gallery, Gitterman Gallery, Ezra Mack

Andre Cypriano Scott Nichols

Czech Photography Hyperion Press, Alan Klotz, Robert Koch

D

Daguerreotypes Charles Isaacs, Charles Schwartz, William L. Schaeffer, Ezra Mack, Wach Gallery

Louise Dahl-Wolfe Hyperion Press, Staley+Wise, Keith de Lellis

John S. Daley McNamara Gallery

Paul D'Amato Daiter Contemporary

Georges Dambier Bonni Benrubi

Bill Dane Fraenkel Gallery

Binh Danh Lisa Sette

William Dassonville Paul M. Hertzmann, Michael Dawson, Joel Soroka, Lee Gallery, Richard Moore, Zur Stockeregg, Joseph Bellows

Judy Dater Scott Nichols, Charles Schwartz, Michael Dawson

Xavier Dauny Esther Woerdehoff

Bruce Davidson RoseGallery, Howard Greenberg, Catherine Edelman

Caroline Davies John Stevenson

John Davies Stephen Cohen, Michael Hoppen

Jen Davis Lee Marks

Lynn Davis Wm. Floyd, Edwynn Houk

Margo Davis Scott Nichols

Scott Davis Michael Shapiro, Michael Dawson

Dawid Priska Pasquer

F. Holland Day Ezra Mack, Silverstein Photography

Lala Deen Dayal Ken & Jenny Jacobson

David Deal Wm. Floyd

Joe Deal Robert Mann

Loomis Dean Keith de Lellis, David Gallery

Mario De Biasi Keith de Lellis, Photology

Raymond De Berquelle Josef Lebovic

Louis De Clercq Hans P. Kraus, Jr., Robert Klein, Alan Klotz, Janet Lehr, Contemporary / Vintage Works, Weston Gallery, Daniel Blau, Gitterman Gallery, Robert Hershkowitz

Cy DeCosse John Stevenson

D. James Dee Steven Kasher

Jack Delano Photographs Do Not Bend, Halsted Gallery

Eduardo del Valle & Mirta Gomez HEMPHILL

Robert Demachy Lee Gallery

Laurence Demaison Esther Woerdehoff

Patrick Demarchelier Staley+Wise

Baron Adolph De Meyer Zur Stockeregg, Contemporary / Vintage Works, Richard Moore

Monica Denevan Scott Nichols

Alyson Denny Alan Klotz

Raymond Depardon Steven Kasher

Wijnanda Deroo Robert Mann

Wouter Deruytter Wessel+O'Connor, David Gallery

Bertrand Desprez Baudoin Lebon

Detroit Photochrome Co. Scott Nichols

Jed Devine Bonni Benrubi

Lucinda Devlin Lee Marks

Carlos Diaz Catherine Edelman

Esteban Pastorino Diaz Photographs Do Not Bend

Seth Dickerman Paul Kopeikin

Goetz Diergarten Kicken Berlin, RoseGallery

André de Dienes Fay Gold, Staley+Wise, Joseph Bellows

Carl De Keyzer Robert Koch

Willem Diepraam Stephen Daiter

Mario Di Girolamo Fay Gold

V. Dijon michèle chomette

Lutz Dille Stephen Bulger

David Dimichele Paul Kopeikin

Edward Dimsdale HackelBury

Jim Dine Pace/MacGill

Frank DiPerna Kathleen Ewing

Stephen DiRado Robert Klein

Mike Disfarmer Howard Greenberg, Steven Kasher

Eugene Disderi Serge Plantureux

John Divola G. Gibson Gallery, Charles Cowles, gallery luisotti

Pete Doherty Stephen Bulger

Robert Doisneau John Cleary, Hyperion Press, Wach Gallery, Keith de Lellis, Staley+Wise, Serge Plantureux, Françoise Paviot, Michael Hoppen, Contemporary / Vintage Works, Gallery 19/21, Johannes Faber, Galerie 1900/2000, Gitterman Gallery, Silverstein Photography, Zabriskie Gallery, Joel Soroka, Paul M. Hertzmann

Desiree Dolron Michael Hoppen

John Dominis David Gallery

Franco Donaggio Joel Soroka

Don Donaghy Photographs Do Not Bend, HEMPHILL

Diana Dopson Stephen L. Clark

Elena Dorfman Edwynn Houk, Robert Klein, Wm. Floyd

Jim Dow RoseGallery, Janet Borden

Marcus Doyle Contemporary / Vintage Works

David Drebin Fahey/Klein

Rod Dresser Weston Gallery

Jean Dreville Contemporary / Vintage Works

Frantisek Drtikol Robert Koch, Zur Stockeregg, Alan Klotz, Charles Schwartz, Joel Soroka, Paul M. Hertzmann, Contemporary / Vintage Works, Johannes Faber, Charles A. Hartman, Priska Pasquer, Gallery 19/21, Galerie 1900/2000, Czech Center, Silverstein Photography

Richard Drury John Cleary

Jacques Dubois Hyperion Press

Pierre Dubreuil Zur Stockeregg, Joel Soroka

Maxime Du Camp William L. Schaeffer, Serge Plantureux, Contemporary / Vintage Works, Ken & Jenny Jacobson, Daniel Blau, Lee Gallery

John Dugdale G. Gibson Gallery, Wessel+O'Connor, Scheinbaum & Russek, Robert Klein

Kerry Dundas Josef Lebovic

Max Dupain Byron McMahon, Josef Lebovic

Rex Dupain Josef Lebovic

Stephen Dupont Byron McMahon

Louis-Emile Durandelle Ken & Jenny Jacobson, Alan Klotz

George Dureau Throckmorton Fine Art

Jay Dusard Etherton Gallery, Stephen L. Clark

Ruth Dusseault Fay Gold

Remy Duval Zabriskie Gallery

Michael Dweck Staley+Wise

Jack Dykinga Etherton Gallery

E

Thomas Eakins Janet Lehr, Contemporary / Vintage Works

Michael Eastman Kathleen Ewing

John B. Eaton Josef Lebovic

Jose Ortiz Echague Joseph Bellows

Dr. Harold Edgerton Etherton Gallery, Robert Koch, Candace Dwan, Joseph Bellows, Photographs Do Not Bend, Howard Greenberg, Scott Nichols

Beth Yarnelle Edwards Robert Klein

William Eggleston Deborah Bell, RoseGallery, Johannes Faber, Photology, Fay Gold, Eric Franck

Josef Ehm Czech Center

Richard Ehrlich Weston Gallery, Fay Gold

Rudolf Eickemeyer Jr. Henry Feldstein, Paul M. Hertzmann, Richard T. Rosenthal

Alfred Eisenstaedt Candace Dwan, David Gallery, Alan Klotz, Howard Greenberg, Michael Shapiro

Arthur Elgort Staley+Wise

Eliot Elisofon HEMPHILL

Martin Elkort John Cleary, Barry Singer

Harry Ellis Richard T. Rosenthal

Peter Elliston Byron McMahon

Michelle Elzay Steven Kasher

Peter Henry Emerson Lee Gallery, Joseph Bellows, Alan Klotz, Ken & Jenny Jacobson, Halsted Gallery, Robert Hershkowitz, Ezra Mack

Alex Emmons Alan Klotz

Marianne Engberg John Stevenson

Morris Engel Stephen Daiter, Photographs Do Not Bend

Lisa Tyson Ennis John Cleary

Janos Enyedi Kathleen Ewing

Mitch Epstein Jackson Fine Art, Yancey Richardson

Robert Erickson Stephen Daiter, Charles A. Hartman

Elizabeth Ernst Catherine Edelman

Elliott Erwitt Candace Dwan, Henry Feldstein, Photo ART, HackelBury, Peter Fetterman, Jackson Fine Art, Robert Koch, A Gallery, Edwynn Houk, Robert Klein, Photographs Do Not Bend, Andrew Smith, Esther Woerdehoff, Etherton Gallery, Joel Soroka

Lalla Essaydi Lisa Sette, Joel Soroka, Edwynn Houk

Dan Estabrook Catherine Edelman

Frank Eugene Richard Moore

Frederick Evans Lee Marks, Hans P. Kraus, Jr., John Stevenson, Paul M. Hertzmann, Lee Gallery, Halsted Gallery, Joseph Bellows, Richard Moore, Janet Lehr, Weston Gallery, Richard T. Rosenthal, Robert Hershkowitz, Ezra Mack, Silverstein Photography

James Evans Stephen L. Clark

Julie Evans Julie Saul

Terry Evans Yancey Richardson, Catherine Edelman, gallery luisotti

Walker Evans Lee Gallery, Robert Mann, Fraenkel Gallery, Zur Stockeregg, Jan Kesner, Lee Marks, Pace/MacGill, Alan Klotz, Wach Gallery, Barry Singer, William L. Schaeffer, Henry Feldstein, Gitterman Gallery, Richard Moore, Janet Lehr, A Gallery, Paul M. Hertzmann, Robert Klein, Halsted Gallery, Michael Shapiro, Edwynn Houk, Robert Miller, Howard Greenberg, Deborah Bell, Contemporary / Vintage Works, Stephen Daiter, Etherton Gallery, Joseph Bellows, G. Gibson Gallery, Charles A. Hartman, Silverstein Photography, gallery luisotti

Macduff Everton Kathleen Ewing, Janet Borden

Samantha Everton Byron McMahon

Karl Ewald argus-fotokunst

Eliane Excoffier Stephen Bulger

Jay Eyerman Daniel Blau

F

Hans Fahrmeyer Throckmorton Fine Art

Charles Famin Richard T. Rosenthal, Serge Plantureux

Nathan Farb Steven Kasher

George R.Fardon Hans P. Kraus, Jr.

Adolf Fassbender Joseph Bellows

Gilbert Fastenaekens Alan Klotz

Bernard Faucon Picture Photo Space

Louis Faurer Hyperion Press, Howard Greenberg, Stephen Cohen, Deborah Bell, Jan Kesner

Irene Fay Barry Singer

Don Fear Kathleen Ewing

Andreas Feininger Bonni Benrubi, David Gallery, Charles Schwartz, Alan Klotz

Harold Feinstein Stephen Cohen, Charles Schwartz, Candace Dwan

Zdenko Fejfar Czech Center

Carole Fekete Baudoin Lebon

Mark Feldstein Zabriskie Gallery

Sandi Fellman Edwynn Houk

Felton-Massinger michèle chomette

Roger Fenton Charles Isaacs, Contemporary / Vintage Works, Hans P. Kraus, Jr., Janet Lehr, Lee Gallery, William L. Schaeffer, Charles Schwartz, Ken & Jenny Jacobson, TARTT/washington, Weston Gallery, Daniel Blau, Robert Hershkowitz

Christina Fernandez gallery luisotti

Caroline Feyt Baudoin Lebon

Frederick Fiebig Ken & Jenny Jacobson, Robert Hershkowitz

Gerard Petrus Fieret Paul M. Hertzmann, Deborah Bell, Charles Isaacs, Gitterman Gallery

John Filo Fahey/Klein

Larry Fink Stephen Cohen

Brian Finke Stephen Cohen

Mario Finocchiaro Keith de Lellis

Arno Fischer argus-fotokunst

Alida Fish Alan Klotz

Steve Fitch Paul Kopeikin, Steven Kasher

J. Bennett Fitts Paul Kopeikin, Julie Saul

Fizeau Hans P. Kraus, Jr., Ezra Mack

Keoki Flagg Wm. Floyd

Trude Fleischmann Hyperion Press, Johannes Faber

Robbert Flick Robert Mann, RoseGallery

Michael Flomen HASTED HUNT

David Fokos Robert Klein, John Cleary, Paul Kopeikin, Jackson Fine Art

Neil Folberg Wach Gallery

Fernand Fonssagrives Michael Hoppen, Bonni Benrubi

Joan Fontcuberta Gitterman Gallery, Zabriskie Gallery

Chip Forelli Candace Dwan

Rena Bass Forman Bonni Benrubi

Henri Foucault Baudoin Lebon

fotoform Kicken Berlin

Allen Frame Gitterman Gallery

Martine Franck Peter Fetterman, HackelBury, Howard Greenberg, Eric Franck

Tapp Francke Jan Kesner

Nine Francois Stephen L. Clark

Jona Frank Paul Kopeikin

Robert Frank Fraenkel Gallery, Hyperion Press, Jan Kesner, Byron McMahon, Lee Marks, Pace/MacGill, Alan Klotz, Zur Stockeregg, Michael Shapiro, Paul M. Hertzmann, Fahey/Klein, Barry Singer, Michael Hoppen, Robert Koch, Etherton Gallery, Johannes Faber, Charles A. Hartman, Michael Dawson, Gitterman Gallery, Edwynn Houk, Richard Moore, Contemporary / Vintage Works, Serge Plantureux, William L. Schaeffer, Silverstein Photography

Deborah Frankel Wm. Floyd

Godfrey Frankel HEMPHILL, Richard T. Rosenthal

Daniel Frasnay Esther Woerdehoff

Janos Frecot Kicken Berlin

C.D. Fredericks Richard T. Rosenthal

Leonard Freed Lee Gallery, Steven Kasher, argus-fotokunst, Esther Woerdehoff, Silverstein Photography

Kate Freedberg Kathleen Ewing

Paul Freeman Byron McMahon

Freeman Bros Josef Lebovic

Charles Freger Kicken Berlin

Jim French/Colt Studio Wessel+O'Connor

French Photography Hyperion Press

Jean-Baptiste Frenet Daniel Blau, Gallery 19/21

René Friede   argus-fotokunst

Anthony Enton Friedkin   Stephen Cohen

Lee Friedlander   Fraenkel Gallery, Lee Marks, Charles Schwartz, Picture Photo Space, Silverstein Photography, TARTT/washington, Gitterman Gallery, Janet Borden, Kicken Berlin, Andrew Smith, Zabriskie Gallery

Amanda Friedman   Paul Kopeikin

Trey Friedman   michèle chomette

George Friedmann   argus-fotokunst

Janet Fries   Kathleen Ewing

Toni Frissell   Staley+Wise

Hayden Fritchley   McNamara Gallery

Francis Frith   Charles Isaacs, Janet Lehr, Alan Klotz, Charles Schwartz, Robert Koch, Lee Gallery, Ezra Mack

Angelo Frontoni   Photology

Elmer Fryer   Richard T. Rosenthal

F.S.A.   Alan Klotz, Jackson Fine Art

Bernhard Fuchs   gallery luisotti

Daniel and Geo Fuchs   Stephen Bulger

Ernst Fuhrmann   Gary Edwards

Shinzo Fukuhara   Charles Schwartz

Masahisa Fukase   Robert Mann

Jaromir Funke   Robert Koch, Alan Klotz, Paul M. Hertzmann, Stephen Daiter, Charles A. Hartman, Joel Soroka, Gallery 19/21, Czech Center

Paul Fusco   Bonni Benrubi, HEMPHILL

Adam Fuss   Fraenkel Gallery, Wm. Floyd

G

Marina Gadonneix   Esther Woerdehoff

Ron Galella   Photology

Galerie Contemporaine   Zabriskie Gallery

Sally Gall   Robert Klein, Julie Saul

Hector Garcia   Throckmorton Fine Art

Alexander Gardner   TARTT/washington, Janet Lehr, Wach Gallery, Lee Gallery, Andrew Smith

Flor Garduño   Throckmorton Fine Art, Photographs Do Not Bend, Fahey/Klein, Etherton Gallery

Terri Garland   Alan Klotz

William Garnett   Scott Nichols, Candace Dwan, Joseph Bellows, Gitterman Gallery, Paul M. Hertzmann, Barry Singer, Richard Moore

Peter Gasser   Zur Stockeregg

Tierney Gearon   Yossi Milo

William Gedney   Howard Greenberg, Gitterman Gallery

Lajos Geenen   Robert Klein

Lynn Geesaman   Stephen Cohen, Jackson Fine Art, Scheinbaum & Russek, Robert Koch, Yancey Richardson, Stephen L. Clark, Catherine Edelman

Andreas Gefeller   HASTED HUNT

Herb Gehr   Charles Schwartz

Jean Geiser   Ken & Jenny Jacobson

Judy Gelles   Stephen Cohen

Juno Gemes   Josef Lebovic

Arnold Genthe   Joseph Bellows, Paul M. Hertzmann, Richard Moore, John Stevenson

Gilles Gerbaud   Françoise Paviot

Rimma Gerlovina/Valeriy Gerlovin   Lisa Sette

Ben Gest   Daiter Contemporary

Luigi Ghirri   Photology, Julie Saul

Mario Giacomelli   Robert Klein, Robert Koch, Henry Feldstein, Howard Greenberg, Alan Klotz, Keith de Lellis, Peter Fetterman, Paul M. Hertzmann, Gallery 19/21, Gitterman Gallery, Photology, Silverstein Photography, Serge Plantureux

Larry Gianettino   HASTED HUNT

Nathaniel W. Gibbons   William L. Schaeffer

David H. Gibson   Wm. Floyd

Ralph Gibson   Hyperion Press, Howard Greenberg, Joel Soroka, Weston Gallery, Etherton Gallery

Ormond Gigli   Staley+Wise

Gilbert & George   Fraenkel Gallery

Bruce Gilden   Silverstein Photography

Leslie Gill   Robert Mann

Laura Gilpin   Andrew Smith, Scheinbaum & Russek, Paul M. Hertzmann

Allen Ginsberg   Howard Greenberg

Paolo Gioli   michèle chomette

André Giroux   Robert Hershkowitz

Giraudon's Artist   Ken & Jenny Jacobson, Charles Isaacs

Gladys Baudoin Lebon

Darren Glass McNamara Gallery

Burt Glinn Steven Kasher

Frank Gohlke Howard Greenberg

Jim Goldberg Pace/MacGill, Stephen Bulger

Rafael Goldchain Stephen Bulger

Nan Golden Janet Lehr

David Goldes Yossi Milo

Nan Goldin Fraenkel Gallery, Gitterman Gallery

Joy Goldkind John Stevenson

Lyle Gomes Michael Shapiro, Halsted Gallery

Debra Goldman G. Gibson Gallery

Andy Goldsworthy HackelBury

Carol Golemboski Robert Klein

Frank Mason Good Ken & Jenny Jacobson

Jean-Paul Goude HASTED HUNT

Linda Adele Goodine Lee Marks

Greg Gorman Fahey/Klein, Wessel+O'Connor

Fritz Goro Daniel Blau

John Gossage Daiter Contemporary

Rudolf Gotsche Czech Center

William Gottlieb Michael Shapiro

Harald Gottschalk Baudoin Lebon

Samuel Gottscho Charles Schwartz, Joel Soroka, Lee Gallery

Elijah Gowin Robert Mann

Emmet Gowin Pace/MacGill, Etherton Gallery, Charles A. Hartman, Wm. Floyd, Joseph Bellows, Paul M. Hertzmann

Mikhail Grachev Nailya Alexander

Brian Graham argus-fotokunst

David Graham Catherine Edelman, Paul Kopeikin, HASTED HUNT, Photographs Do Not Bend

Katy Grannan Fraenkel Gallery

John Grant Kathleen Ewing

Angela Grauerholz Françoise Paviot

Edward Grazda Deborah Bell, Gitterman Gallery

Stanley Greenberg Candace Dwan

J. B. Greene Hans P. Kraus, Jr., Janet Lehr, Robert Koch, Robert Klein, Robert Hershkowitz, Ezra Mack

Milton Greene Staley+Wise

Lauren Greenfield Robert Koch, Pace/MacGill, Fahey/Klein

Fergus Greer Michael Hoppen

William K. Greiner Photographs Do Not Bend

Kimberly Gremillion Halsted Gallery

Joel Grey John Stevenson

Antonin Gribovsky Czech Center

Kelly Grider Throckmorton Fine Art

Ken Griffiths Michael Hoppen

Philip Jones Griffiths Steven Kasher

Alexander Grinberg Nailya Alexander

Lori Grinder Nailya Alexander

Renato Grome Byron McMahon

Jan Groover Janet Borden

Walter Grossman Wach Gallery

Group f-64 Scott Nichols

Bedrich Grunzweig John Stevenson

Grzeszykowska & Smaga Robert Mann

Victor Guidalevitch Gallery 19/21

Tomasz Gudzowaty Stephen Bulger

John Guider John Stevenson

Ara Güler argus-fotokunst

F.C. Gundlach Photo ART, Kicken Berlin

Shi Guorui Alan Klotz, Charles Schwartz

Sunil Gupta Stephen Bulger

John Gutmann Fraenkel Gallery, Michael Shapiro, Barry Singer

Rosalie Gwathmey Charles A. Hartman

H

Manuel H Serge Plantureux

Ernst Haas Johannes Faber, Michael Hoppen, Zur Stockeregg, Silverstein Photography, Wach Gallery

Steven Haas Throckmorton Fine Art

Johan Hagemeyer Paul M. Hertzmann, Scott Nichols, Richard Moore, Joel Soroka, Michael Shapiro, William L. Schaeffer

Raymond Hains Françoise Paviot

Karel Hajek Zabriskie Gallery

Miroslav Hak Czech Center

Heinz Hajek-Halke Priska Pasquer

Gail Albert Halaban Robert Mann

Fiona Hall Josef Lebovic

Ruth Hallensleben Photo ART

Philippe Halsman Charles Schwartz, Wach Gallery, Howard Greenberg, Johannes Faber, Barry Singer

Ilkka Halso Photology

Neil Hamon McNamara Gallery

Hiroshi Hamaya Steven Kasher, Michael Hoppen

W. Hammerschmidt Ken & Jenny Jacobson

Robert F. Hammerstiel michèle chomette

Alexander Hammid Czech Center

Hand-colored photographs William L. Schaeffer

Werner Hannappel michèle chomette

Duane Hanson Laurence Miller

Jitka Hanzlová Kicken Berlin

Rick Hards Lisa Sette

Bert Hardy William L. Schaeffer

Aspassio Haronitaki Barry Friedman Ltd.

Richard Harrington Stephen Bulger

Alex Harris Scheinbaum & Russek

Lena Scott Harris Henry Feldstein, Richard T. Rosenthal

Pat Harris Paul M. Hertzmann

Paul Hartigan McNamara Gallery

Roy Hartling Stephen Bulger

Cig Harvey Joel Soroka

Declan Haun Joseph Bellows

V. Tony Hauser John Stevenson

Raoul Hausmann Gallery 19/21, Zabriskie Gallery, Serge Plantureux

Paul Haviland Paul M. Hertzmann, Lee Gallery

Ron Haviv HASTED HUNT

Jefferson Hayman Michael Shapiro, John Cleary

F. Jay Haynes Gitterman Gallery

Dave Heath Stephen Bulger, Barry Singer, Howard Greenberg, Charles A. Hartman

William Heick Paul M. Hertzmann, Michael Shapiro

Herman Heid Ken & Jenny Jacobson

Jean-Jacques Heilmann michèle chomette

Robert Heinecken Pace/MacGill, Barry Singer, Joseph Bellows

Adriel Heisey Etherton Gallery, Kathleen Ewing

Beatrice Helg Joel Soroka

Konrad Helbig Photo ART

Petr Helbig Czech Center

Derek Henderson McNamara Gallery

Fritz Henle Henry Feldstein, Charles Schwartz, Throckmorton Fine Art

Nicholaas Henneman Hans P. Kraus, Jr., Ezra Mack

Florence Henri Robert Koch, Galerie 1900/2000, Silverstein Photography

Bill Henson Josef Lebovic, Robert Miller

Brandon Herman David Gallery, Wessel+O'Connor, David Gallery

Gaylord Herron Robert Burge

Matt Herron Steven Kasher

Lucien Herve Michael Hoppen

Antoinette Hervey Keith de Lellis

Elizabeth Heyert Edwynn Houk

Yuichi Hibi Michael Dawson

Todd Hido RoseGallery

Chester Higgins, Jr. Peter Fetterman, Scott Nichols

Peter Higdon Stephen Bulger

Brett Hilder Josef Lebovic

Hill & Adamson Hans P. Kraus, Jr., Janet Lehr, Charles Isaacs, Lee Gallery, Charles Schwartz, Contemporary / Vintage Works, Halsted Gallery, Richard T. Rosenthal, Robert Hershkowitz, Ezra Mack, William L. Schaeffer

Lejaren Hiller Keith de Lellis

Jack Hillers Janet Lehr

John Hillers William L. Schaeffer, Etherton Gallery, Paul M. Hertzmann, Robert Koch, Andrew Smith

David Hilliard Jackson Fine Art, Yancey Richardson

Rob Hillier Josef Lebovic

Paul Himmel Keith de Lellis

John Hinde Wessel+O'Connor

Lewis Hine Stephen Daiter, Lee Gallery, Lee Marks, Alan Klotz, Bonni Benrubi, Zur Stockeregg, Charles Schwartz, Barry Singer, Halsted Gallery, Joseph Bellows, Robert Klein, Steven Kasher, Paul M. Hertzmann, Keith de Lellis, Charles A. Hartman, Richard Moore, Zabriskie Gallery, Michael Shapiro, William L. Schaeffer, Jan Kesner

Hiro Lee Marks

J

Joseph Jachna   Stephen Daiter

William H. Jackson   Janet Lehr, Alan Klotz, William L. Schaeffer, Etherton Gallery, Halsted Gallery, Wach Gallery, Gitterman Gallery, Charles Isaacs, Charles Schwartz, Richard T. Rosenthal**,** Andrew Smith

Lotte Jacobi   Gallery 19/21, michèle chomette, Gary Edwards, Paul M. Hertzmann, Zabriskie Gallery

Bill Jacobson   Robert Klein, G. Gibson Gallery, Julie Saul

Jodie Vicenta Jacobson   Yancey Richardson

Monique Jacot   Esther Woerdehoff

Jacquelin / Darbelley   michèle chomette

Bertha Jacques   Gary Edwards

Pierre Jahan   michèle chomette, Gitterman Gallery, Zabriskie Gallery

Adam Jahiel   Etherton Gallery, Candace Dwan, Stephen L. Clark, John Cleary

Hana Jakrlova   Eric Franck

Don James   Ariel Meyerowitz

Franz Jantzen   HEMPHILL

Allan Janus   Kathleen Ewing

Japan   Alan Klotz

Japanese Ambrotypes   Charles Schwartz

Japanese Pictorialist & Modernists   Charles Schwartz

Japanese Propaganda Photographs   Charles Schwartz

Stefan Jasienski   Zur Stockeregg

Allan Jenkins   HackelBury

John Jenkins III   G. Gibson Gallery

Len Jenshel   Kathleen Ewing, Joseph Bellows

Vaclav Jirasek   Czech Center

Mimmo Jodice   Baudoin Lebon

Simen Johan   Yossi Milo, Robert Koch

John Johns   McNamara Gallery

Paul Johns   McNamara Gallery

Eirik Johnson   Yossi Milo, G. Gibson Gallery

Sarah Anne Johnson   Stephen Bulger, Julie Saul

Alfred Cheney Johnston   Contemporary / Vintage Works

Rev. Calvert Jones   Hans P. Kraus, Jr., Janet Lehr, Robert Hershkowitz, Ezra Mack

Charles Jones   Howard Greenberg

Colin Jones   Michael Hoppen

Pirkle Jones   Michael Shapiro

Chris Jordan   Paul Kopeikin

Kenneth Josephson   Yancey Richardson, Stephen Daiter

K

Guillermo Kahlo   Throckmorton Fine Art

Kahn & Selesnick   Paul Kopeikin, Yancey Richardson, Lisa Sette

Maira Kalman   Julie Saul

Clemens Kalisher   argus-fotokunst

Simpson Kalisher   Keith de Lellis

Karol Kállay   argus-fotokunst

Clemens Kalischer   Argus fotokunst

Grit Kallin-Fischer   Priska Pasquer

Harri Kallio   Bonni Benrubi

Richard Kalvar   Steven Kasher

Nadav Kander   Yancey Richardson, Fahey/Klein

Ruth Kaplan   Stephen Bulger

Sid Kaplan   Deborah Bell

James Karales   Steven Kasher

Yousuf Karsh   Yancey Richardson, Wach Gallery, Robert Klein, Robert Koch, Weston Gallery, Andrew Smith, A Gallery, Halsted Gallery

Gertrude Kasebier   Lee Gallery, William L. Schaeffer, Charles Isaacs, Keith de Lellis, Paul M. Hertzmann Alan Klotz, Richard Moore

Barbara Kasten   gallery luisotti

Kunihiko Katsumata   Picture Photo Space

John Kauffmann   Josef Lebovic

Rinko Kawauchi   Priska Pasquer

Misty Keasler   Photographs Do Not Bend

Peter Keetman   Photo ART

Dorothea Kehaya   Zur Stockeregg

Dusan Keim   Wm. Floyd

Michelle Keim   Catherine Edelman

Seydou Keïta   HackelBury

Pertti Kekarainen Photology

Thomas Kellner Stephen Cohen

Robb Kendrick Stephen L. Clark

Michael Kenna Catherine Edelman, Jackson Fine Art, Robert Klein, Picture Photo Space, Robert Mann, John Cleary, Halsted Gallery, Photographs Do Not Bend, G. Gibson Gallery, HackelBury, Weston Gallery, Gitterman Gallery, Charles A. Hartman, Joseph Bellows

David Michael Kennedy HackelBury Stephen L. Clark

Gyorgy Kepes Stephen Daiter, Joel Soroka, Robert Koch, Michael Shapiro, Scott Nichols

Lisa Kereszi Yancey Richardson

Geof Kern Fahey/Klein

Pascal Kern HackelBury, Zabriskie Gallery

Sean Kernan Gallery 19/21

Charles Kerry Josef Lebovic

André Kertész Stephen Bulger, John Cleary, Peter Fetterman, Jackson Fine Art, Robert Koch, Michael Senft, A Gallery, Michael Shapiro, Wach Gallery, Howard Greenberg, Staley+Wise, Zur Stockeregg, Charles Schwartz, Barry Singer, Yancey Richardson, Henry Feldstein, Hyperion Press, Fahey/Klein, Weston Gallery, Paul M. Hertzmann, Halsted Gallery, Stephen Daiter, Etherton Gallery, HackelBury, Byron McMahon, Gitterman Gallery, Gallery 19/21, Contemporary / Vintage Works, Johannes Faber, Priska Pasquer, William L. Schaeffer, Charles A. Hartman, Michael Dawson, michèle chomette, Alan Klotz, Robert Klein, Joseph Bellows, Edwynn Houk, Scott Nichols, Scheinbaum & Russek, Silverstein Photography, Zabriskie Gallery, Charles Isaacs

Mark Kessell Stephen Bulger

Robert Glenn Ketchum Wach Gallery

Doug Keyes G. Gibson Gallery

Yevgeny Khaldey Robert Koch, Nailya Alexander

Yakov Khalip Nailya Alexander

Idris Khan Fraenkel Gallery

Anselm Kiefer Daniel Blau

Kusakabe Kimbei TARTT/washington, Ken & Jenny Jacobson

Henry King Josef Lebovic

Isodore von Kinsbergen Ken & Jenny Jacobson

Imre Kinszki Robert Koch, Alan Klotz

Stefan Kirkeby Michael Shapiro

Heidi Kirkpatrick G. Gibson Gallery

Albert Kish Stephen Bulger

Kazuo Kitai Picture Photo Space

Steven Klein Janet Lehr, Staley+Wise, Wessel+O'Connor

William Klein Fahey/Klein, Howard Greenberg, Michael Hoppen, Byron McMahon, Peter Fetterman, HackelBury, Robert Klein, Hyperion Press, Zabriskie Gallery

Chad Kleitsch Ariel Meyerowitz

Mark Klett Etherton Gallery, Pace/MacGill, Paul Kopeikin, Lisa Sette

Stuart Klipper Candace Dwan

Gustav Klutsis Priska Pasquer

Gary Knight HASTED HUNT

Alan Knowles McNamara Gallery

Matthias Koch Esther Woerdehoff

Nikolai Kokx McNamara Gallery

Bob Kolbrener Fay Gold

Ola Kolehmainen Robert Miller

François Kollar Gitterman Gallery, Gallery 19/21, Zabriskie Gallery, Contemporary / Vintage Works

Martin Kollar Kathleen Ewing

Michiko Kon Picture Photo Space

Bogdan Konopka Françoise Paviot, Candace Dwan

Bohn Chang Koo Photographs Do Not Bend, HASTED HUNT

Viktor Kopasz Czech Center

Rudolf Koppitz Johannes Faber, Gallery 19/21, Kicken Berlin, Silverstein Photography, Wessel+O'Connor

Fred G. Korth Wm. Floyd

Yasuko Kotani Picture Photo Space

August Kotzsch Ken & Jenny Jacobson

Josef Koudelka Robert Koch, Pace/MacGill, Eric Franck, Michael Shapiro

Anthony Koutras Stephen Bulger

Paul Kozal Scott Nichols, Weston Gallery

Myron Kozman Charles A. Hartman

Daniel Kramer Staley+Wise

Antonin Kratochvil HASTED HUNT

George Krause   Photographs Do Not Bend

Shai Kremer   Julie Saul

Annelise Kretschmer   Priska Pasquer

Les Krims   Baudoin Lebon

Vilem Kriz   Scott Nichols, Joseph Bellows, John Stevenson, Barry Singer

Germaine Krull   Henry Feldstein, Gallery 19/21, Priska Pasquer, Françoise Paviot, Galerie 1900/2000, Edwynn Houk, Contemporary / Vintage Works, michèle chomette

Nikolai Kubeev   Nailya Alexander

Nissa Kubly   Lisa Sette

Hiroji Kubota   Steven Kasher

Heinrich Kühn   Zur Stockeregg, Lee Gallery, Paul M. Hertzmann, William L. Schaeffer, Johannes Faber, Halsted Gallery, John Stevenson, Wach Gallery

Mona Kuhn   Scott Nichols, Charles Cowles, G. Gibson Gallery, Jackson Fine Art

Valentina Kulagina   Priska Pasquer

Norman Kulkin   Steven Kasher

Claudia Kunin   Michael Dawson

Vladimir Kuprianov   Nailya Alexander

Koichiro Kurita   Scott Nichols, John Stevenson

Masatomo Kuriya   Yancey Richardson

L

David LaChapelle   Staley+Wise, Fahey/Klein, Photology

Joachim Ladefoged   HASTED HUNT

Mark Laita   Fahey/Klein

Joe Lalli   Throckmorton Fine Art

Maureen Lambray   Stephen Cohen

Christopher Landis   Michael Dawson

Bob Landry   Daniel Blau

Dorothea Lange   Edwynn Houk, John Cleary, Paul M. Hertzmann, Lee Gallery, Scott Nichols, Janet Lehr, Alan Klotz, RoseGallery, Michael Shapiro, Richard Moore, William L. Schaeffer,

Jason Langer   Michael Shapiro, Bonni Benrubi

Col. Jean-Charles Langlois   Contemporary / Vintage Works

Ida G. Lansky   Photographs Do Not Bend

Harry Lapow   Alan Klotz

William Larson   Charles Isaacs

Jacques-Henri Lartigue   Hyperion Press, Staley+Wise, Henry Feldstein, Michael Hoppen, Contemporary / Vintage Works, G. Gibson Gallery, Gallery 19/21, Bonni Benrubi, Robert Klein, gallery luisotti

Gillian Laub   Bonni Benrubi

Clarence John Laughlin   Joseph Bellows, Robert Miller, Stephen Daiter, A Gallery, Contemporary / Vintage Works

Juan Laurent   Gary Edwards

Jan Lauschmann   Joel Soroka, Richard T. Rosenthal, Czech Center

Siegfried Lauterwasser   Photo ART

Karine Laval   Bonni Benrubi

Frank Lavelle   Kathleen Ewing

Alma Lavenson   Michael Shapiro

Tony Law   Wm. Floyd

Louise Lawler   Steven Kasher

Stephen Lawson   Kathleen Ewing

Laszlo Layton   Peter Fetterman

Adolf Lazi   Photo ART

Dinh Q. Le   Photology

Marcus Leatherdale   John Stevenson

Robert LeBeau   Robert Burge

Robert Lebeck   argus-fotokunst

Edmond Lebel   Serge Plantureux

Felix Auguste Leclerc   michèle chomette

LeDien & Le Gray   Hans P. Kraus, Jr.

Rene Ledoux-Lebard   Serge Plantureux

Jocelyn Lee   Pace/MacGill

Russell Lee   Charles Schwartz, Richard Moore, Alan Klotz

Till Leeser   Photo ART

Gustave Le Gray   Charles Isaacs, Robert Koch, Janet Lehr, William L. Schaeffer, Zur Stockeregg, Contemporary / Vintage Works, Hans P. Kraus, Jr., Weston Gallery, Daniel Blau, Gallery 19/21, Robert Hershkowitz, Ezra Mack

Laurence Le Guay   Josef Lebovic

Janne Lehtinen   Photology

Annie Leibovitz   Fahey/Klein, Edwynn Houk, Andrew Smith, Jackson Fine Art

Neil Leifer David Gallery

Anne Leigniel Gallery 19/21

Guillaume Leingre michèle chomette

Arthur Leipzig Howard Greenberg, HackelBury, Peter Fetterman, Jackson Fine Art

Saul Leiter Howard Greenberg

Reiner Leist Julie Saul

Guillaume Lemarchal michèle chomette

Erna Lendvai-Dircksen Steven Kasher

Erica Lennard Staley+Wise

Gary Leonard Michael Dawson

Herman Leonard Catherine Edelman, Fahey/Klein, Byron McMahon, A Gallery, Andrew Smith, Jackson Fine Art

Sze Tsung Leong Yossi Milo

Rebecca Lepkoff Howard Greenberg

Dany Leriche Baudoin Lebon

Chrystele Lerisse Baudoin Lebon

Nathan Lerner Stephen Daiter, Michael Senft

Helmar Lerski Kicken Berlin

Henri Le Secq Hans P. Kraus, Jr., Contemporary / Vintage Works, Robert Koch, Robert Hershkowitz

Laura Letinsky Robert Klein, Stephen Bulger, Joseph Bellows, Yancey Richardson

Lance Letscher Stephen L. Clark

Mikael Levin michèle chomette

Robert Levin Alan Klotz

Wayne Levin Robert Koch

Joel D. Levinson Barry Singer, Contemporary / Vintage Works

Leon Levinstein Stephen Daiter, Howard Greenberg

David Levinthal Fay Gold, Lisa Sette

Ethan Levitas Paul Kopeikin

Helen Levitt Fraenkel Gallery, Laurence Miller, Robert Klein, Deborah Bell, Paul Kopeikin, Jackson Fine Art, Stephen Daiter, Peter Fetterman, G. Gibson Gallery, Contemporary / Vintage Works, Silverstein Photography

Jon Lewis Josef Lebovic

Jonathan Lewis Bonni Benrubi

Sol LeWitt Fraenkel Gallery

Katia Liebmann HackelBury

Jeff Chien-Hsing Liao Julie Saul

LIFE Photographers Alan Klotz, John Cleary

Ken Light Barry Singer

Michael Light Robert Klein

Malcom Lightner Wm. Floyd

Heather Lin Charles Isaacs

Edwin Hale Lincoln William L. Schaeffer, Lee Gallery

Fay Sturtevant Lincoln Richard T. Rosenthal

Charles Lindsay Wm. Floyd, Gitterman Gallery

J. W. Lindt Josef Lebovic

O. Winston Link Catherine Edelman, Robert Mann, Robert Klein, Peter Fetterman, Candace Dwan, Robert Burge, Etherton Gallery, Andrew Smith, Scheinbaum & Russek

Peter Lippmann Barry Singer

Achim Lippoth Priska Pasquer, John Stevenson

Georgy Lipskerov Nailya Alexander

El Lissitzky Edwynn Houk, Priska Pasquer

Herbert List Photo ART, Stephen Daiter, Fahey/Klein, Stephen Bulger, Wessel+O'Connor, Robert Miller

J. D. Llewelyn Hans P. Kraus, Jr.

August Loeffler William L. Schaeffer

John Loengard David Gallery

Loewy & Puiseux Joseph Bellows

Lon of New York Throckmorton Fine Art

Phillip Lorca di Corcia Pace/MacGill

Eli Lotar Françoise Paviot, michèle chomette

Pascal Loubet Esther Woerdehoff

O. Rufus Lovett Stephen L. Clark

Jacques Lowe Peter Fetterman

Elmar Ludwig RoseGallery

Karel Ludwig Czech Center

Jan Lukas Hyperion Press, Keith de Lellis, Czech Center

Michelle Luke Wm. Floyd

Monte Luke Josef Lebovic

Charles Lummis Charles Schwartz, Michael Dawson

Birgitta Lund Julie Saul

Harry H. Lunn Estate Baudoin Lebon

Deborah Luster Catherine Edelman

Joshua Lutz   Gitterman Gallery

Loretta Lux   Yossi Milo

Mary Ann Lynch   John Stevenson

Mark Lynch   Wessel+O'Connor

George Platt Lynes   Keith de Lellis, John Stevenson, Throckmorton Fine Art, Wessel+O'Connor, Howard Greenberg, Robert Miller

Danny Lyon   Etherton Gallery, Hyperion Press, Scott Nichols, Fahey/Klein, Charles A. Hartman, Edwynn Houk, Silverstein Photography, Steven Kasher

Nathan Lyons   TARTT/washington, Silverstein Photography

Robert Lyons   Paul Kopeikin

M

Dora Maar   Robert Koch, Lee Marks, Stephen Daiter, Galerie 1900/2000

C. Cameron Macauley   Paul M. Hertzmann, Michael Dawson

Ian Macdolald   McNamara Gallery

Ian MacEachern   Stephen Bulger

Julie Mack   Laurence Miller

Ulrich Mack   argus-fotokunst

Barbara Macklowe   Halsted Gallery

Alex MacLean   Kathleen Ewing

Robert MacPherson   Hans P. Kraus, Jr., Alan Klotz, Ken & Jenny Jacobson, Robert Hershkowitz

Victor Macarol   Zur Stockeregg

Michal Macku   John Stevenson

Neeta Madahar   Julie Saul

Chema Madoz   Photographs Do Not Bend, Robert Klein, Lisa Sette, Esther Woerdehoff

Andreas Magdanz   Janet Borden

MAGNUM Agency Photographers   Stephen Bulger

Rene Magritte   Silverstein Photography, Robert Miller

Ute Mahler   argus-fotokunst

Eugene Mailand   michèle chomette

David Maisel   Paul Kopeikin

E.J. Major   Stephen Bulger

David Malin   Edwynn Houk

Henri Mallard   Josef Lebovic

Luis Mallo   Stephen Bulger, HASTED HUNT, Throckmorton Fine Art

Mike Mandel   gallery luisotti

Ann Mandelbaum   Françoise Paviot

Mark Mann   Laurence Miller

Sally Mann   Picture Photo Space, Wm. Floyd, Jackson Fine Art, Robert Koch, Byron McMahon, TARTT/washington, Edwynn Houk

Esko Männikkö   Yancey Richardson

Constantine Manos   Steven Kasher

Man Ray   Robert Mann, Janet Lehr, Robert Koch, Joel Soroka, Michael Senft, Zur Stockeregg, Hyperion Press, Paul M. Hertzmann, Keith de Lellis, Fahey/Klein, Fraenkel Gallery, Françoise Paviot, Contemporary / Vintage Works, Serge Plantureux, Gallery 19/21, Weston Gallery, Barry Friedman Ltd., Galerie 1900/2000, Edwynn Houk, Gary Edwards, TARTT/washington, Zabriskie Gallery, Silverstein Photography, Johannes Faber, Robert Miller

Werner Mantz   Wm. Floyd, Priska Pasquer, Kicken Berlin, Silverstein Photography

Barbara Maples   Photographs Do Not Bend

Robert Mapplethorpe   Fahey/Klein, Fay Gold, Weinstein Gallery, Weston Gallery, Ezra Mack, Wessel+O'Connor, Jan Kesner

Gaudenzio Marconi   Daniel Blau

Tanya Marcuse   HEMPHILL

Etienne-Jules Marey   michèle chomette, Hans P. Kraus, Jr.

Mary Ellen Mark   Fahey/Klein, Yancey Richardson, Jackson Fine Art

Kurt Markus   Staley+Wise, Photology

Marcel Marien   Contemporary / Vintage Works

F. T. Marinetti   Priska Pasquer

Fred Maroon   Kathleen Ewing

Jim Marshall   Fahey/Klein

Maria Martinez-Cañas   Julie Saul

Dunja Marton   argus-fotokunst

Charles Marville   Charles Isaacs, Robert Koch, Lee Gallery, Hans P. Kraus, Jr., Françoise Paviot, Contemporary / Vintage Works, Weston Gallery, Alan Klotz, Howard Greenberg, Robert Hershkowitz

Daniel Masclet   Keith de Lellis, Gitterman Gallery

Didier Massard   Baudoin Lebon, Julie Saul, Robert Klein

Didier Dearborn Massar Joseph Bellows

Margrethe Mather Paul M. Hertzmann

Leo Matiz Throckmorton Fine Art, Throckmorton Fine Art

Herbert Matter Staley+Wise

Mary Mattingly Robert Mann

Paul Maurer Zabriskie Gallery

John Max Stephen Bulger

Robert Maxwell Fahey/Klein

Elaine Mayes Robert Burge

Roger Mayne Barry Singer, Gitterman Gallery

Albert Maysles Steven Kasher

Wilhelm Maywald Zabriskie Gallery

Sanaz Mazinani Stephen Bulger

Paolo Mazzanti Fay Gold

Angus McBean Photographs Do Not Bend, Richard T. Rosenthal

Will McBride Photo ART, argus-fotokunst, Johannes Faber

Robert McCabe Gary Edwards

Graham McCarter Josef Lebovic

Linda McCartney HackelBury, Bonni Benrubi

Lindsay McCrum Fay Gold

Steve McCurry Peter Fetterman

Fred W. McDarrah Steven Kasher

Cecil McDonald Jr. Catherine Edelman

McDermott & McGough Wm. Floyd, Weinstein Gallery

Robert McFarlane Josef Lebovic

Sally McInerney Josef Lebovic

Bruce McKaig Kathleen Ewing

Meredith McKinney Kathleen Ewing

Judith McMillan Bonni Benrubi

Michael C. McMillen gallery luisotti

Laura McPhee Bonni Benrubi, G. Gibson Gallery

Ralph Eugene Meatyard TARTT/washington, Charles A. Hartman, Fraenkel Gallery, Paul M. Hertzmann, Stephen Daiter

François Mechain michèle chomette

Raymond Meeks Jackson Fine Art, Candace Dwan

Leon Eugene Mehedin Contemporary / Vintage Works

Susan Meiselas RoseGallery, Daiter Contemporary

Paul Meleschnig Wm. Floyd

Georges Melies Serge Plantureux

Douglas Mellor Robert Klein, Robert Burge

Tony Mendoza Stephen Cohen

Tina Mérandon Gallery 19/21

Corinne Mercadier Alan Klotz

Olivier Meriel Candace Dwan, Esther Woerdehoff

Jeff Mermelstein Steven Kasher

Roger Mertin Joseph Bellows

John Metoyer John Stevenson

Ray K. Metzker Laurence Miller, Françoise Paviot, Jackson Fine Art

Sheila Metzner John Stevenson, Staley+Wise

Joel Meyerowitz Zabriskie Gallery, Picture Photo Space, Edwynn Houk, Ariel Meyerowitz

Duane Michals Robert Koch, Pace/MacGill, Fahey/Klein

Diana Michener Pace/MacGill

Middle East Alan Klotz

Maria Miesenberger Robert Mann

Nino Migliori Keith de Lellis

Richard Mikhailov Pace/MacGill

Gary Fabian Miller HackelBury

Lee Miller Staley+Wise, Byron McMahon

Tyagan Miller Lee Marks

Wayne F. Miller Keith de Lellis, Lee Gallery, Stephen Daiter

Jean-Francois Millet Ezra Mack

Laurent Millet Robert Mann

Joseph Mills HEMPHILL

Jeffrey Milstein Paul Kopeikin, Bonni Benrubi

Byung-Hun Min Baudoin Lebon, Peter Fetterman

Dodo Jin Ming Laurence Miller, Michael Hoppen

Roger Minick Jan Kesner

Arno Rafael Minkkinen Robert Klein, Fay Gold, Barry Friedman Ltd.

Paul-Emile Miot michèle chomette

Leonard Misonne   Keith de Lellis, Joseph Bellows, Joel Soroka, Halsted Gallery

Richard Misrach   Catherine Edelman, Etherton Gallery, Fraenkel Gallery, Jan Kesner, HackelBury, Zur Stockeregg, Pace/MacGill, G. Gibson Gallery, Robert Mann, Photology

Benn Mitchell   Keith de Lellis

Ryuji Miyamoto   Kicken Berlin

Lisette Model   Robert Mann, HASTED HUNT, Baudoin Lebon, gallery luisotti

Andrea Modica   Catherine Edelman, Edwynn Houk, G. Gibson Gallery

Tina Modotti   Paul M. Hertzmann, Throckmorton Fine Art, Edwynn Houk, Photology, Jan Kesner

Lucia Moholy   Gallery 19/21

Laszlo Moholy-Nagy   Robert Koch, Stephen Daiter, Zur Stockeregg, Edwynn Houk, Paul M. Hertzmann, Françoise Paviot, Charles A. Hartman, William L. Schaeffer, Charles Isaacs

Evgeny Mokhorev   Nailya Alexander

Pierre Molinier   Galerie 1900/2000

Carlo Mollino   Photology

Andrei Molodkin   Priska Pasquer

Darrow Montgomery   Kathleen Ewing

Delilah Montoya   Photographs Do Not Bend

Beth Moon   John Stevenson

Karl Moon   Etherton Gallery, Richard T. Rosenthal, William L. Schaeffer

Sarah Moon   Howard Greenberg, Michael Hoppen, Weinstein Gallery

Andrew Moore   Yancey Richardson, Jackson Fine Art

Charles Moore   Steven Kasher, Howard Greenberg

David Moore   Josef Lebovic

Henry Moore   Johannes Faber, Ezra Mack, Silverstein Photography

Jean Moral   Gitterman Gallery

John Moran   William L. Schaeffer

Inge Morath   Howard Greenberg, Barry Singer, Johannes Faber, Esther Woerdehoff

Abelardo Morell   Catherine Edelman, Bonni Benrubi, Michael Hoppen

Barbara Morgan   Wach Gallery, Silverstein Photography, Halsted Gallery, Contemporary / Vintage Works

Bert Morgan   Wessel+O'Connor

Willard Morgan   Wach Gallery

Daido Moriyama   Picture Photo Space, Michael Dawson, Michael Hoppen, Priska Pasquer, Charles A. Hartman, Stephen Cohen

Lewis Morley   Byron McMahon, gallery luisotti

Christopher Morris   HASTED HUNT

Wright Morris   Paul M. Hertzmann, Etherton Gallery, Halsted Gallery, Joseph Bellows, Weston Gallery, G. Gibson Gallery, Serge Plantureux, Lee Gallery

Ralph Morse   David Gallery

Viggo Mortensen   Stephen Cohen

William Mortensen   Paul M. Hertzmann, Halsted Gallery, Joseph Bellows, Henry Feldstein, Richard Moore, Contemporary / Vintage Works

Ray Mortenson   Janet Borden

Lida Moser   Stephen Bulger

F. J.-A Moulin   Ken & Jenny Jacobson

Alphonse Mucha   Gary Edwards

Mugshots   Steven Kasher

Ugo Mulas   Photology

Martina Mullaney   Yossi Milo

Karin Apollonia Müller   Julie Saul

Vic Muniz   Janet Lehr

Martin Munkacsi   Howard Greenberg, Michael Hoppen

Portia Munson   HEMPHILL

Nicholas Muray   Fahey/Klein, Joseph Bellows, Photographs Do Not Bend, Joel Soroka, Richard T. Rosenthal

Colin Murray   Ken & Jenny Jacobson

Dr. John Murray   Charles Schwartz, Hans P. Kraus, Jr., Contemporary / Vintage Works

Eadweard Muybridge   Etherton Gallery, Janet Lehr, Lee Gallery, Robert Koch, Robert Klein, Michael Dawson, Alan Klotz, TARTT/washington, Lee Marks, Paul M. Hertzmann, Laurence Miller, Joseph Bellows, Fraenkel Gallery, Richard Moore, Charles Schwartz, Throckmorton Fine Art, Wessel+O'Connor, Weston Gallery, Françoise Paviot, Andrew Smith, William L. Schaeffer, Wessel+O'Connor

Carl Mydans   David Gallery

Joan Myers   Kathleen Ewing

N

NASA   Gary Edwards, Charles Isaacs, Charles Schwartz, Daniel Blau

James Nachtwey   Fahey/Klein, HASTED HUNT

Nadar   Janet Lehr, Hans P. Kraus, Jr., Alan Klotz, Robert Hershkowitz

Peter Nadas   Kicken Berlin

Yoshimitsu Nagasaka   Weston Gallery

Takashi Nakagawa   Picture Photo Space

Edmund Nägele   RoseGallery

Rajesh Nair   Kathleen Ewing

Mosei Nappelbaum   Nailya Alexander

Marie Navarre   Lisa Sette

Carlo Naya   Richard T. Rosenthal

Genevieve Naylor   Staley+Wise

Robin Neate   McNamara Gallery

Jürgen Nefzger   Françoise Paviot

Charles Negre   Charles Isaacs, Hans P. Kraus, Jr., Contemporary / Vintage Works, Françoise Paviot, michèle chomette, Daniel Blau, Gallery 19/21, Robert Klein, Janet Lehr, Weston Gallery, Lee Gallery, Robert Hershkowitz, Ezra Mack

Kendall Nelson   Kathleen Ewing

Mario Cravo Neto   Robert Koch, Yancey Richardson, Throckmorton Fine Art, Esther Woerdehoff

Vladimir Neubert   Czech Center

Beaumont Newhall   Scheinbaum & Russek

Nancy Newhall   Scheinbaum & Russek

Arnold Newman   Commerce Graphics, Howard Greenberg, Halsted Gallery, HackelBury, Peter Fetterman, Bonni Benrubi, Kicken Berlin, Andrew Smith, Paul M. Hertzmann, Wach Gallery

Marvin Newman   Keith de Lellis, Stephen Daiter, Charles A. Hartman, Silverstein Photography

Helmut Newton   Fahey/Klein, Wm. Floyd, Janet Lehr, Staley+Wise, Byron McMahon, Johannes Faber, A Gallery, Kicken Berlin, Photology

New York City/19th&20th Century   Charles Schwartz

Han Nguyen   Joseph Bellows

Loan Nguyen   Esther Woerdehoff

Dianora Niccolini   Throckmorton Fine Art

James Nicholls   Scott Nichols

Karla G. Nicholson   Kathleen Ewing

Walter Niedermayr   Robert Miller

Simone Nieweg   gallery luisotti

Artur Nikodem   Robert Mann

Morten Nilsson   Photographs Do Not Bend

Leonard Nimoy   Bonni Benrubi

Hermann Nitsch   Johannes Faber

Lori Nix   G. Gibson Gallery, Stephen Cohen

Nicholas Nixon   Fraenkel Gallery, Yossi Milo, Charles A. Hartman, Zabriskie Gallery

Anne Noble   McNamara Gallery

David Noble   RoseGallery

Marshall Noice   John Cleary

Tanja Nola   McNamara Gallery

Simon Norfolk   Bonni Benrubi, gallery luisotti

Dorothy Norman   Michael Shapiro, Contemporary / Vintage Works

Sonya Noskowiak   Lee Gallery, Paul M. Hertzmann, Michael Shapiro, Michael Dawson, Richard Moore, Scott Nichols

Ira Nowinski   Michael Dawson

Said Nuseibeh   Scott Nichols

O

Misako Oba   Gary Edwards

Will Hiroshi Oda & Lisa Oda   John Stevenson

Michael O' Brien   Photographs Do Not Bend

Pavel Odvody   Photo ART

P.H. Oelman   Henry Feldstein

Max Oettli   McNamara Gallery

Brian Oglesbee   Fay Gold

Ken Ohara   Stephen Cohen

Frederick Ohringer   Joel Soroka

Erwin Olaf   HASTED HUNT

Matthias Olmeta   Serge Plantureux

Michael O'Neill   Etherton Gallery

Yuji Ono   Baudoin Lebon

Cas Oorthuys   Paul M. Hertzmann

Elizabeth Opalenik   John Stevenson

Suzanne Opton   Stephen Cohen

John O'Reilly   Julie Saul

John Pfahl Johannes Faber, Joseph Bellows, Janet Borden

Brent Phelps John Cleary

Charles Phoenix Michael Dawson

Photo League John Cleary

Nata Piaskowski Paul M. Hertzmann

Pablo Picasso Johannes Faber

Patricia Piccinini Robert Miller

Denis Piel Staley+Wise

Jack Pierson Photology, Robert Miller

Vincenzo Pietropaolo Stephen Bulger

William H. Pigou Ken & Jenny Jacobson

Matthew Pillsbury Bonni Benrubi, Jackson Fine Art, Michael Hoppen

Melissa Ann Pinney Catherine Edelman, Alan Klotz

Eugene Piot Daniel Blau

Gerald Pisarzowski Stephen Bulger

Bernard Plossu michèle chomette

David Plowden Catherine Edelman, Laurence Miller, Peter Fetterman

Guglielmo Pluschow Zabriskie Gallery

Axel Poignant Josef Lebovic

Robert Polidori RoseGallery, Weinstein Gallery, Edwynn Houk

Herbert Ponting Ken & Jenny Jacobson

Eliot Porter Scheinbaum & Russek, Andrew Smith, Picture Photo Space, Henry Feldstein, Wach Gallery, Joseph Bellows, Photographs Do Not Bend, Alan Klotz, Richard Moore, Richard T. Rosenthal, HASTED HUNT

William B. Post William L. Schaeffer

David Potts Josef Lebovic

Georges Poulet Daniel Blau

Antoine Poupel Françoise Paviot

Mark Power (American) Kathleen Ewing

Enrico Prampolini Priska Pasquer

Charles Pratt Robert Mann, Wm. Floyd

Len Prince Staley+Wise

Michael Prince David Gallery

Jean Pascal Princiaux michèle chomette

J. John Priola Joseph Bellows

Nicholas Prior Yossi Milo

Krzysztof Pruszkowski Contemporary / Vintage Works

Gonzalo Puch Julie Saul

Rico Puhlmann Staley+Wise

Rosamond Purcell Kathleen Ewing

Constant Puyo Contemporary / Vintage Works, Richard Moore

Q

F. W. Quandt Paul M. Hertzmann

Edward Quigley Joel Soroka, Keith de Lellis, Alan Klotz, Johannes Faber

Edward Quinn Michael Hoppen

Philip Quirk Josef Lebovic

R

Hervé Rabot michèle chomette

Arnulf Rainer Johannes Faber

Orit Raff Julie Saul

Susan Rankaitis Robert Mann

Rankin Fahey/Klein

Michael Rauner Scott Nichols

Robert Rauschenberg Pace/MacGill

François-Auguste Ravier michèle chomette

Lilo Raymond John Stevenson

Beverly Rayner G. Gibson Gallery

Olivier Rebufa Baudoin Lebon

Robert Redfield Janet Lehr

Dede Reed Joel Soroka

Lou Reed Steven Kasher

John Reef Kathleen Ewing

Louis Regnault Hans P. Kraus, Jr.

Vilém Reichmann Johannes Faber, Gitterman Gallery, Czech Center

Wolfgang Reichmann Johannes Faber

Rejlander Hans P. Kraus, Jr., Janet Lehr

Richard Renaldi Yossi Milo, Jackson Fine Art

René-Jacques Hyperion Press, Françoise Paviot, Zabriskie Gallery

Albert Renger-Patszch   Henry Feldstein,Photo ART, Zur Stockeregg, Johannes Faber, Priska Pasquer, Paul M. Hertzmann, Barry Singer, michèle chomette, Kicken Berlin, Zabriskie Gallery, Silverstein Photography

Bruno Requillart   Zabriskie Gallery

Res   Lisa Sette, Robert Mann

Jacques Reutlinger   Zabriskie Gallery

Giles Revell   Michael Hoppen

Nancy Rexroth   Weinstein Gallery, Robert Mann, Charles A. Hartman

Antonio Reynoso   Throckmorton Fine Art

Jorge Ribalta   Zabriskie Gallery

Marc Riboud   Howard Greenberg, HackelBury

J.B. Rich   Richard T. Rosenthal

Dr. Albert Richards   Candace Dwan

Eugene Richards   HASTED HUNT

Bob Richardson   Staley+Wise

Robert Richardson   Kathleen Ewing

Terry Richardson   Michael Hoppen

William D. Richardson   Gitterman Gallery

Ira Richer   Steven Kasher

Robert Richfield   Alan Klotz

Robert Yarnell Richie   Richard T. Rosenthal

Brad Richman   Lee Marks

Evelyn Richter   argus-fotokunst

Hans Richter   Michael Senft

Liz Rideal   HackelBury

Heinrich Riebesehl   Kicken Berlin, gallery luisotti

Leni Riefenstahl   Fahey/Klein, Richard T. Rosenthal

Richard Riley   William L. Schaeffer

Roberto Rincon   Throckmorton Fine Art

F. A. Rinehart   Etherton Gallery

ringl & pit   Robert Mann

Angelika Rinnhofer   Paul Kopeikin

Miguel Rio Branco   Galerie 1900/2000

Murray Riss   Joseph Bellows

William Rittase   Wm. Floyd, Photographs Do Not Bend, Richard T. Rosenthal

Herb Ritts   Staley+Wise, Robert Klein, Fahey/Klein, G. Gibson Gallery, Fay Gold, Steven Kasher, Wessel+O'Connor

Willy Rizzo   Eric Franck

Louis Robert   Hans P. Kraus, Jr., Janet Lehr, Charles Isaacs, Contemporary / Vintage Works, Robert Hershkowitz

Holly Roberts   Etherton Gallery, Catherine Edelman

Grace Robertson   John Cleary, Kathleen Ewing, Peter Fetterman

Natalie Robertson   McNamara Gallery

James Robertson   Ken & Jenny Jacobson

H. P. Robinson   Janet Lehr, Ken & Jenny Jacobson, TARTT/washington

Lisa Robinson   Paul Kopeikin

Alexander Rodchenko   Robert Koch, Priska Pasquer, Zur Stockeregg, Johannes Faber, Steven Kasher, Nailya Alexander, Edwynn Houk, Photology, Silverstein Photography

George Rodger   Barry Singer, Steven Kasher, Richard Moore

Auguste Rodin   Serge Plantureux

Jaroslav Roessler   Hyperion Press, Robert Koch, Johannes Faber, Priska Pasquer, Czech Center

Howard Roffman   Wessel+O'Connor

Milton Rogovin   gallery luisotti

Franz Roh   Gitterman Gallery

Werner Rohde   Photo ART

Willy Ronis   Kathleen Ewing, Jackson Fine Art, Hyperion Press, Peter Fetterman, Byron McMahon, HackelBury, John Cleary, Halsted Gallery, Contemporary / Vintage Works, Gallery 19/21

Tata Ronkholz   gallery luisotti

William Ropp   Gallery 19/21

Franz Rosenbaum   Stephen Bulger

Ken Rosenthal   Etherton Gallery, Michael Dawson

Donald Ross   Paul M. Hertzmann

Horatio Ross   Hans P. Kraus, Jr., Janet Lehr

Judith Joy Ross   Pace/MacGill

Alison Rossiter   Stephen Bulger

Jaroslav Rössler   see Roessler

Theodore Roszak   Gitterman Gallery, Zabriskie Gallery

Lukas Roth   Paul Kopeikin

Sanford Roth   Scott Nichols

Aaron Rothman   Gitterman Gallery

Amalie Rothschild Staley+Wise, David Gallery

Arthur Rothstein John Cleary, Alan Klotz, Gitterman Gallery, Halsted Gallery, Richard Moore, Janet Lehr, Barry Singer, Wach Gallery

Jono Rotman McNamara Gallery

Paolo Roversi Pace/MacGill

Michal Rovner Pace/MacGill

Anne Rowland HEMPHILL

Ernestine Ruben John Stevenson

Leo Rubinfien Robert Mann

Eva Rubinstein John Cleary

Charlotte Rudolph michèle chomette

Albert Rudomine Gary Edwards, michèle chomette

Michael Ruetz Priska Pasquer

Ariel Ruiz i Altaba Esther Woerdehoff

Ed Ruscha Yancey Richardson

Janet Russek Scheinbaum & Russek

Andrew Joseph Russell Janet Lehr, William L. Schaeffer, Michael Dawson, Wach Gallery, Andrew Smith

Rae Russel Barry Singer, Charles A. Hartman

Russian Photography Robert Koch

Mark Ruwedel Françoise Paviot, Stephen Bulger, gallery luisotti

Drahomir Josef Rüzicka Henry Feldstein, Joseph Bellows, Johannes Faber, Joel Soroka, Czech Center

Victoria Ryan Kathleen Ewing, John Stevenson

Ryuijie Gallery 19/21

S

Bauer Sa Throckmorton Fine Art

Josephine Sacabo Catherine Edelman, Stephen L. Clark, John Stevenson, A Gallery

Michal Ronnen Safdie Robert Klein, David Gallery

Lorry Salcedo-Mitrani Throckmorton Fine Art, Photographs Do Not Bend

Sebastião Salgado Scheinbaum & Russek, Yancey Richardson, Fahey/Klein, Byron McMahon, Peter Fetterman, Robert Klein, HackelBury, Michael Shapiro, Weinstein Gallery

David Salle Robert Miller

Jacqueline Salmon michèle chomette

Erich Salomon HASTED HUNT

Auguste Salzmann Charles Isaacs, Hans P. Kraus, Jr., Alan Klotz, Janet Lehr, Contemporary / Vintage Works, Ken & Jenny Jacobson, Lee Gallery, Robert Hershkowitz, Ezra Mack

Lucas Samaras Pace/MacGill

Vicki Sambunaris Yancey Richardson

Haruhika Sameshima McNamara Gallery

Pentti Sammallahti Scott Nichols, Candace Dwan, John Cleary

Unai San Martin Scott Nichols

Judy Sanchez Kathleen Ewing

August Sander Kathleen Ewing, Fraenkel Gallery, Picture Photo Space, Deborah Bell, Halsted Gallery, Yancey Richardson, Priska Pasquer, gallery luisotti

Allessandra Sanguinetti Yossi Milo

Lise Sarfati Yossi Milo, RoseGallery

Hiro Sato Picture Photo Space

Jan Saudek Robert Koch, Johannes Faber, A Gallery, Czech Center, Jan Kesner

William Saunders TARTT/washington

Henri Sauvaire michèle chomette

Charles R. Savage Andrew Smith

Igor Savchenko Gary Edwards, Nailya Alexander

Lynn Saville Yancey Richardson, Paul Kopeikin

Emile Savitry Zabriskie Gallery

Tomoko Sawada Zabriskie Gallery

Carol Sawyer G. Gibson Gallery

Christian Schad Silverstein Photography

Robert A. Schaefer, Jr. Wm. Floyd

Steve Schapiro Fahey/Klein

Howard Schatz David Gallery

Jerry Schatzberg Staley+Wise, Peter Fetterman

David Scheinbaum Scheinbaum & Russek

Sherill Schell Contemporary / Vintage Works

Walter Schels Photo ART

Rocky Schenck Catherine Edelman, Michael Shapiro, Jackson Fine Art, Stephen L. Clark, Etherton Gallery

Frank Scherschel Daniel Blau

Robert Schiller Gitterman Gallery

Burkhard Schittny Photo ART

Hans-Christian Schink Kicken Berlin

Carolee Schneemann Charles Isaacs

Gary Schneider Daiter Contemporary, Julie Saul

Toni Schneiders Photo ART

Martin Schoeller HASTED HUNT

Sarah Schorr Yancey Richardson

Victor Schrager HackelBury, Edwynn Houk

Charlie Schreiner Contemporary / Vintage Works

Wilhelm Schuermann Kicken Berlin

Flip Schulke Keith de Lellis

Laurel Schultz G. Gibson Gallery

Gundula Schulze el Dowy Deborah Bell, TARTT/washington, argus-fotokunst

George Schumacher Joseph Bellows

Wilhelm Schürmann gallery luisotti

Bill Schwab Halsted Gallery

Larry Schwarm Robert Koch

Dona Schwartz Stephen Bulger

Edward Schwartz Paul M. Hertzmann

Joe Schwartz Michael Shapiro, John Cleary

Rudolf Schwarzkogler Johannes Faber

Ernst Schwitters Gitterman Gallery

Michel Szulc-Krzyzanowski Baudoin Lebon

David Scopick Stephen Bulger

Gregory Scott Catherine Edelman

Roger Scott Josef Lebovic

Charles Scowen Ken & Jenny Jacobson, William L. Schaeffer, Joseph Bellows

Pascal Sebah Ken & Jenny Jacobson

Tazio Secchiaroli Photology, Serge Plantureux

Volker Seding Stephen Bulger

Albert Seeberger Zabriskie Gallery

George Seeley Lee Gallery, Halsted Gallery, William L. Schaeffer

Floyd Segel Kathleen Ewing

Frederich Seidenstuker Michael Hoppen

Tomio Seike Robert Klein, Picture Photo Space

Alfred Seiland Zur Stockeregg, Kicken Berlin

Peter Sekaer Howard Greenberg, Richard Moore

Mark Seliger Fahey/Klein, Byron McMahon

Neil Selkirk Lee Marks

Oreste Selvatico gallery luisotti

Greg Seman Halsted Gallery

Tanjuci Senji Zur Stockeregg

Vincent Serbin John Stevenson

Andres Serrano Photology

Jose Maria Sert michèle chomette

Susan Seubert G. Gibson Gallery

Ivan Shagin Nailya Alexander

Ben Shahn Howard Greenberg, Paul M. Hertzmann, Richard Moore, Janet Lehr, Richard T. Rosenthal, Silverstein Photography

Arkady Shaikhet Nailya Alexander

Paul Shambroom Weinstein Gallery

Stephen Shames Steven Kasher

Mark Shaw David Gallery, Keith de Lellis

Art Shay Stephen Daiter

Bernard Shea Horne Keith de Lellis

Diana Shearwood Stephen Bulger

Robert Sheer Michael Dawson

Charles Sheeler Edwynn Houk, Silverstein Photography

Fazal Sheikh Pace/MacGill

Ann Shelton McNamara Gallery

Cindy Sherman Janet Lehr, HackelBury

Toshio Shibata Laurence Miller, Françoise Paviot, gallery luisotti

William Gordon Shields William L. Schaeffer, Stephen Bulger

Osamu Shiihara Priska Pasquer

Sergey Shimansky Nailya Alexander

Stephen Shore TARTT/washington, Edwynn Houk, Kicken Berlin

Julius Shulman Jackson Fine Art, Yancey Richardson

Hugh Shurley John Stevenson

Malik Sidibe HackelBury

Jeanloup Sieff Staley+Wise, Baudoin Lebon

Arthur Siegel Stephen Cohen, Stephen Daiter, Silverstein Photography

Elizabeth Siegfried Stephen Bulger

Wolfgang Sievers Josef Lebovic

Bernard Silberstein Throckmorton Fine Art

George Silk Daniel Blau

Javier Silva Meinel Throckmorton Fine Art

Larry Silver Silverstein Photography

Marilyn Silverstone Steven Kasher

Jeffrey Silverthorne Photographs Do Not Bend

Camille Silvy William L. Schaeffer

Art Sinsabaugh Stephen Daiter, Lee Marks, Charles A. Hartman

Clara Sipprell Richard T. Rosenthal

Aaron Siskind Etherton Gallery, Robert Mann, Stephen Daiter, Michael Shapiro, Howard Greenberg, Robert Klein, Paul M. Hertzmann, Scheinbaum & Russek, Henry Feldstein, Scott Nichols, Barry Singer, William L. Schaeffer, Joseph Bellows, Charles A. Hartman, G. Gibson Gallery, Gitterman Gallery, Halsted Gallery, Silverstein Photography

William Louis Henry Skeen Ken & Jenny Jacobson

Sandy Skoglund Fay Gold, A Gallery

Christian Skrein Priska Pasquer

Neal Slavin Photographs Do Not Bend

Matthew Sleeth Josef Lebovic

Gerald Slota HASTED HUNT

Luke Smalley Wessel+O'Connor

Boris Smelov Gary Edwards, Nailya Alexander, Serge Plantureux

Claudia Smigrod Kathleen Ewing

Beuford Smith Steven Kasher

Heide Smith Josef Lebovic

Kiki Smith Pace/MacGill

Lindy Smith Bonni Benrubi

Mike Smith Jackson Fine Art, Yancey Richardson, Robert Koch, Lee Marks, Scott Nichols

Patti Smith Robert Miller

Robin Smith Josef Lebovic

Rodney Smith Robert Klein, Fahey/Klein, John Cleary

Ross T. Smith McNamara Gallery

W. Eugene Smith Andrew Smith, Howard Greenberg, Stephen Daiter, Robert Mann, Wach Gallery, Charles Schwartz, Scott Nichols, Barry Singer, Halsted Gallery, Henry Feldstein, William L. Schaeffer,

Lee Gallery, Lee Marks, Etherton Gallery, Charles A. Hartman, Alan Klotz, A Gallery, Contemporary / Vintage Works, Michael Shapiro, Daniel Blau, Silverstein Photography

Tracey Snelling Stephen Cohen

Kenneth Snelson Laurence Miller

Lawrence Snider Halsted Gallery, David Gallery

Herb Snitzer Barry Singer, Stephen Bulger

James Thrall Soby Charles Schwartz

Melvin Sokolsky Staley+Wise, Fahey/Klein

Camille Solyagua Joseph Bellows, Charles A. Hartman

Frederick Sommer Pace/MacGill, Stephen Daiter, Paul M. Hertzmann, Etherton Gallery, Charles A. Hartman

Giorgio Sommer TARTT/washington, Ken & Jenny Jacobson

Emilio Sommariva Keith de Lellis

Alec Soth Weinstein Gallery

Ettore Sottsass Photology

Will Soule Michael Dawson

Jem Southam Charles Isaacs, Robert Mann

Southworth and Hawes Janet Lehr, Contemporary / Vintage Works, Hans P. Kraus, Jr., William L. Schaeffer

Jerry Spagnoli Contemporary / Vintage Works

Michael Spano Laurence Miller

Vee Speers Byron McMahon

Cathy Spence Stephen L. Clark

Ema Spencer Keith de Lellis

Jack Spencer Catherine Edelman, Jackson Fine Art, Stephen L. Clark

Peter Sramek Stephen Bulger

Peter Stackpole Barry Singer, Scott Nichols, David Gallery

Nicki Stager HASTED HUNT

Anton Stankowski Zur Stockeregg

John Stanmeyer HASTED HUNT

Doug and Mike Starn Fay Gold, Weinstein Gallery, HackelBury, Lisa Sette

Bohumil Stastny Joel Soroka, Czech Center

Elfriede Stegemeyer Priska Pasquer

Edward Steichen   Janet Lehr, Paul M. Hertzmann, Hyperion Press, Zur Stockeregg, Lee Gallery, Staley+Wise, Keith de Lellis, TARTT/ washington, Henry Feldstein, Joel Soroka, Howard Greenberg, William L. Schaeffer, Halsted Gallery, Contemporary / Vintage Works, Wach Gallery, Hans P. Kraus, Jr., Weston Gallery, A Gallery, Gitterman Gallery, Richard Moore, Andrew Smith, Zabriskie Gallery, Michael Shapiro, Richard T. Rosenthal, Candace Dwan, Ezra Mack, Silverstein Photography

Amy Stein   Paul Kopeikin

Uwe Steinberg   argus-fotokunst

Albert Steiner   Zur Stockeregg

André Steiner   Gallery 19/21

Ralph Steiner   Robert Klein, Scheinbaum & Russek, Charles Schwartz, Henry Feldstein, Halsted Gallery

Otto Steinert   Kicken Berlin, Contemporary / Vintage Works, Priska Pasquer

Mark Steinmetz   Jackson Fine Art, Yancey Richardson

David Stephenson   Julie Saul

Stereoviews   William L. Schaeffer

Joseph Sterling   Stephen Daiter, Charles A. Hartman

Andrea Stern   HASTED HUNT

Bert Stern   Staley+Wise, Fahey/Klein, Janet Lehr

Lynn Stern   Scott Nichols

Phil Stern   Fahey/Klein, Staley+Wise

Joel Sternfeld   Charles Schwartz

Louis Stettner   Bonni Benrubi

Iain Stewart   G. Gibson Gallery, Julie Saul

John Stewart   Staley+Wise

Alfred Stieglitz   Bonni Benrubi, Zur Stockeregg, Janet Lehr, Alan Klotz, William L. Schaeffer, Robert Mann, Lee Gallery, Pace/MacGill, Andrew Smith, Paul M. Hertzmann, Weston Gallery, Joseph Bellows, Wach Gallery, A Gallery, Gitterman Gallery, Edwynn Houk, Richard Moore, Scheinbaum & Russek, Zabriskie Gallery, Contemporary / Vintage Works, Silverstein Photography

W.J. Stillman   Gary Edwards

Robert Stivers   Throckmorton Fine Art

Dennis Stock   HackelBury, Steven Kasher

Sarah Stolfa   Silverstein Photography

Story - Maskelyne   Hans P. Kraus, Jr.

Lou Stoumen   Barry Singer, Contemporary / Vintage Works

Paul Strand   Paul M. Hertzmann, Robert Mann, Scott Nichols, Edwynn Houk, Lee Gallery, William L. Schaeffer, Howard Greenberg, Michael Shapiro, Zur Stockeregg, Joseph Bellows, Weston Gallery, Richard Moore, Andrew Smith, Wach Gallery, Throckmorton Fine Art, Zabriskie Gallery, Ezra Mack, Silverstein Photography

Zoe Strauss   Silverstein Photography

Jindrich Streit   Eric Franck

Guy Stricherz: Americans in Kodachrome 1945-1965   RoseGallery

Christer Stroemholm   Kicken Berlin

Tony Stromberg   Candace Dwan

Carl Struewe   Johannes Faber

Karl Struss   Lee Gallery, William L. Schaeffer, Zur Stockeregg, Charles Schwartz, Henry Feldstein, Paul Kopeikin, Halsted Gallery, Joel Soroka, Joseph Bellows, Richard Moore, Paul M. Hertzmann, Silverstein Photography

Jock Sturges   Robert Klein, Scott Nichols, Etherton Gallery, Robert Koch, Stephen Bulger, Photographs Do Not Bend, Fahey/Klein, Johannes Faber

Edward Sturr   Joseph Bellows

John Stryker   Photographs Do Not Bend

Issei Suda   Picture Photo Space, Charles A. Hartman

Josef Sudek   Paul M. Hertzmann, Robert Koch, Howard Greenberg, Joel Soroka, Zur Stockeregg, Alan Klotz, Henry Feldstein, Johannes Faber, Stephen Cohen, Stephen Daiter, Contemporary / Vintage Works, Halsted Gallery, Charles A. Hartman, Priska Pasquer, Gallery 19/21, michèle chomette, Weston Gallery, Barry Friedman Ltd., Richard T. Rosenthal, Czech Center

Hiroshi Sugimoto   Fraenkel Gallery, Robert Klein, HackelBury, Michael Hoppen, Priska Pasquer

Larry Sultan   Janet Borden

H.Y. Summons   Richard T. Rosenthal

Elisabeth Sunday   Zur Stockeregg

Ladislav Sutnar   michèle chomette

Frank Meadow Sutcliffe   Lee Gallery, Ken & Jenny Jacobson, Wach Gallery

Gerardo Suter   Throckmorton Fine Art

Antanas Sutkus   Nailya Alexander, argus-fotokunst

Ferenc Suto   Throckmorton Fine Art

Jan Svoboda Czech Center

Arne Svenson Jan Kesner, Julie Saul

Luke Swank Serge Plantureux

Julianne Swartz Lisa Sette

Elaine Pelot Syron Josef Lebovic

Joseph Szabo Gitterman Gallery, Michael Hoppen

Steve Szabo Kathleen Ewing, HackelBury

John Szarkowski Pace/MacGill, Peter Fetterman

Gabor Szilasi Stephen Bulger

T

Maurice Tabard Hyperion Press, Michael Senft, Galerie 1900/2000, Gitterman Gallery, Charles A. Hartman

Isaiah W. Taber William L. Schaeffer, Richard Moore

Jerry Takigawa Weston Gallery

W. H. Fox Talbot Hans P. Kraus, Jr., Janet Lehr, Alan Klotz, Robert Koch, Robert Klein, Weston Gallery, Charles Isaacs, Robert Hershkowitz, Ezra Mack

Benjamin C. Tankersley Kathleen Ewing

Allan Tannenbaum Steven Kasher

Dr. Dain L. Tasker Joseph Bellows

Tato Priska Pasquer

Maggie Taylor Laurence Miller, John Cleary, Fay Gold, Weston Gallery

Mark Tedeschi Josef Lebovic

Rolf Teitgans Keith de Lellis

Val Telberg Laurence Miller

Brad Temkin Stephen Bulger, Scott Nichols

Joyce Tenneson Fay Gold, Joel Soroka

Mayumi Terada Robert Miller

Adolphe Terris Contemporary / Vintage Works, michèle chomette

Edmund Teske Stephen Cohen, Scott Nichols, Barry Singer, Stephen Daiter

Textbraun Baudoin Lebon

Felix Teynard Hans P. Kraus, Jr., William L. Schaeffer, Alan Klotz, Weston Gallery, Robert Hershkowitz

Felix Thiollier michèle chomette

Jeff Thomas Stephen Bulger

Lew Thomas Barry Singer

John Thomson Janet Lehr, Ken & Jenny Jacobson, William L. Schaeffer

Dr. Max Thorek Etherton Gallery

Otmar Thormann michèle chomette

Ruth Thorne-Thomsen Catherine Edelman, Laurence Miller, Françoise Paviot

John Thomson Robert Hershkowitz

Paul Thuile Photology

George Tice Robert Klein, John Cleary, Scott Nichols, Candace Dwan, Peter Fetterman, Ariel Meyerowitz, Halsted Gallery

Miroslav Tichy Michael Hoppen

Louis Comfort Tiffany Gary Edwards

Bill Timmerman Joseph Bellows

Tintypes Steven Kasher, William L. Schaeffer, Ezra Mack

Alexey Titarenko Nailya Alexander, David Gallery, Gary Edwards

Hamish Tocher McNamara Gallery

Laurena Toledo Throckmorton Fine Art

Claude Tolmer Keith de Lellis

Lisa Tomasetti Byron McMahon

Anna Tomczak Kathleen Ewing

Jonathan Torgovnik Stephen Cohen, Alan Klotz

Michael Torosian Stephen Bulger

Patrick Tosani Zabriskie Gallery

Eileen Toumanoff Kathleen Ewing

Larry Towell Stephen Bulger

Philip Trager John Stevenson

Gerard Traquandi Zabriskie Gallery

Charles Traub Gitterman Gallery

Anton Josef Trcka Johannes Faber

Remigijus Treigys Nailya Alexander

Pierre Tremaux Ken & Jenny Jacobson

Arthur Tress Scott Nichols, Throckmorton Fine Art, Esther Woerdehoff, Joseph Bellows, Contemporary / Vintage Works

Linnaeus Tripe Charles Isaacs, Robert Koch, Hans P. Kraus, Jr., Janet Lehr, Weston Gallery, Contemporary / Vintage Works, Lee Gallery, Robert Hershkowitz, Ezra Mack

Riwan Tromeur michèle chomette

Hiromi Tsuchida Michael Hoppen

Joaquin Trujillo   RoseGallery

Holger Trülzsch   michèle chomette

Hitoshi Tsukiji   Picture Photo Space

Albrecht Tübke   RoseGallery

Tung-Hing   TARTT/washington

Deborah Turbeville   Staley+Wise

Katherine Turczan   Yossi Milo

James Turrell   Lisa Sette

B. B. Turner   Hans P. Kraus, Jr.

Peter Turnley   Lee Marks

Pekka Turunen   Stephen Bulger

Ingeborg Tyssen   Byron McMahon

U

Shoji Ueda   Picture Photo Space

Jerry Uelsmann   Fay Gold, Laurence Miller, Weston Gallery, Halsted Gallery, A Gallery, Robert Klein

Philippe Ughetto   HackelBury

Vasily Ulitin   Nailya Alexander

Lloyd Ullberg   Barry Singer, Gitterman Gallery, Richard T. Rosenthal

Doris Ulmann   William L. Schaeffer, Keith de Lellis, Paul M. Hertzmann

Brian Ulrich   Julie Saul, Robert Koch

Umbo   Priska Pasquer, Kicken Berlin, Silverstein Photography

Susan Unterberg   Yancey Richardson

Eda Urbani   Photology

Takatomo Usui   G. Gibson Gallery

Nick Ut   Fahey/Klein

Burk Uzzle   Laurence Miller

V

Franco Vaccari   Photology

John Vachon   Richard Moore

Mandy Vahabzadeh   Joel Soroka

Roger Vail   Michael Dawson

Beatrice Valdes Paz   Nailya Alexander

Alfredo Valente   Keith de Lellis

Marc Valesella   Wm. Floyd

Julien Vallou de Villeneuve   Janet Lehr, Ezra Mack, Contemporary / Vintage Works

Rudy Vanderlans   Michael Dawson

John Vanderpant   Paul M. Hertzmann, Barry Singer

William Vandivert   Daniel Blau

Geza Vandor   Contemporary / Vintage Works

George H. Van Anda   Richard T. Rosenthal

Ian Van Coller   Lisa Sette

Ed Van Der Elsken   Kicken Berlin

Frank Van Der Salm   Jan Kesner

James Van Der Zee   Howard Greenberg, Steven Kasher, Kathleen Ewing, Gitterman Gallery

Ron Van Dongen   Jackson Fine Art, Peter Fetterman, Catherine Edelman, Bonni Benrubi, G. Gibson Gallery

Willard Van Dyke   Scheinbaum & Russek, Paul M. Hertzmann, Richard Moore

Ruud Van Empel   Jackson Fine Art

Sarah Van Keuren   John Stevenson

Bertien Van Manen   Yancey Richardson

Hellen Van Manen   Yancey Richardson

Pim Van Os   Paul M. Hertzmann

Juliet Van Otteren   John Cleary

David Van Royen   McNamara Gallery

Carl Van Vechten   William L. Schaeffer

Cassio Vasconcellos   Photographs Do Not Bend

Ben Vautier   Zabriskie Gallery

Claudio Vazquez   Kathleen Ewing

Bernar Venet   michèle chomette

Adriene K. Veninger   Jan Kesner, Robert Klein

Paolo Ventura   HASTED HUNT

JoAnn Verburg   G. Gibson Gallery, Pace/MacGill

Chris Verene   Photographs Do Not Bend

Camilo Jose Vergara   RoseGallery

Vernacular Photographs   Richard T. Rosenthal

David Vestal   Robert Mann

Joseph Vigier   Hans P. Kraus, Jr.

Louis Vignes   michèle chomette

André Villers   Michael Hoppen

Roman Vishniac Howard Greenberg, Joel Soroka, Barry Singer

Massimo Vitali Bonni Benrubi,

Alexandre Vitkine HackelBury, Laurent Herschtritt

Vivex Prints Richard T. Rosenthal

Raymond Voinquel Wessel+O'Connor

Carola Vogt/Peter Boerboom Priska Pasquer

Wilhelm Von Gloeden Throckmorton Fine Art, Keith de Lellis, Wessel+O'Connor, Zabriskie Gallery

Michel Von Graffenried Esther Woerdehoff

Baron Von Stillfried Ken & Jenny Jacobson

Ellen Von Unwerth Staley+Wise

Chris Von Wangenheim Staley+Wise

Adam Clark Vroman Lee Marks, Michael Dawson, Richard Moore, Andrew Smith

W

Peter M. Wach Wach Gallery

Bob "Daddy-O" Wade Stephen L. Clark

Catherine Wagner gallery luisotti

Walery Keith de Lellis

Thomas Walther Daniel Blau

Andy Warhol Pace/MacGill, Daniel Blau, Silverstein Photography

Harry Warnecke Charles Schwartz, Richard T. Rosenthal

Hiroshi Watanabe Bonni Benrubi

Carleton E. Watkins Charles Isaacs, Lee Gallery, Robert Koch, Janet Lehr, Scott Nichols, Zur Stockeregg, William L. Schaeffer, Richard Moore, Paul M. Hertzmann, Fraenkel Gallery, Halsted Gallery, Weston Gallery, Alan Klotz, Robert Klein, Ezra Mack, Wach Gallery, Andrew Smith, Contemporary / Vintage Works

Margaret Watkins Robert Mann

Dan Weaks Zur Stockeregg

Alex Webb Catherine Edelman, Joseph Bellows, Etherton Gallery, Stephen Bulger, HASTED HUNT

Jonathan Webb Throckmorton Fine Art

Todd Webb Scheinbaum & Russek, Yancey Richardson, Lee Gallery, Barry Singer, Charles Schwartz, Richard T. Rosenthal

Tenesh Webber John Cleary

Bruce Weber Fahey/Klein, Throckmorton Fine Art

Christine Webster McNamara Gallery

Charles Weed Paul M. Hertzmann

Eric Weeks Jackson Fine Art

Weegee Bonni Benrubi, Johannes Faber, Howard Greenberg, Lee Gallery, Michael Hoppen, Robert Mann, Keith de Lellis, Henry Feldstein, William L. Schaeffer, Stephen Cohen, Zabriskie Gallery, Michael Shapiro, Richard T. Rosenthal, Silverstein Photography

William Wegman Pace/MacGill, Picture Photo Space, Robert Klein, Lisa Sette

Ryan Weideman Silverstein Photography

Terri Weifenbach Jackson Fine Art, Robert Klein, Daiter Contemporary

Greg Weight Josef Lebovic

Dan Weiner Howard Greenberg, Robert Mann

Robert Weingarten Weston Gallery

Sabine Weiss Candace Dwan Contemporary / Vintage Works

Ai Weiwei Robert Miller

Nathaniel Welch Fahey/Klein

Jack Welpott Barry Singer

Eudora Welty John Cleary

Lionel Wendt Throckmorton Fine Art

Alfred Wertheimer Staley+Wise

Len Wesney McNamara Gallery

Henry Wessel Charles Cowles, Robert Mann, gallery luisotti

Angela West Jackson Fine Art

Randy West Jan Kesner, Silverstein Photography

Eva Skold Westerlind G. Gibson Gallery

Western Photo Guild Wessel+O'Connor

Brett Weston Robert Koch, Paul M. Hertzmann, Michael Shapiro, Scott Nichols, G. Gibson Gallery, Wach Gallery, Scheinbaum & Russek, Gitterman Gallery, Robert Klein, Zur Stockeregg, Henry Feldstein, Halsted Gallery, Joseph Bellows, Etherton Gallery, Joel Soroka, Lee Gallery, Barry Singer, Contemporary / Vintage Works, Jan Kesner, Charles A. Hartman, Weston Gallery, A Gallery, Edwynn Houk, Richard Moore, William L. Schaeffer, Richard T. Rosenthal, Silverstein Photography

Cole Weston Wach Gallery, Halsted Gallery, Weston Gallery

Edward Weston   Robert Klein, Fraenkel Gallery, Paul M. Hertzmann, Janet Lehr, Robert Koch, Michael Shapiro, Halsted Gallery, Scheinbaum & Russek, Alan Klotz, Howard Greenberg, A Gallery, Scott Nichols, Wach Gallery, William L. Schaeffer, Zur Stockeregg, Barry Singer, Throckmorton Fine Art, Henry Feldstein, Fahey/Klein, Lee Gallery, Joel Soroka, Joseph Bellows, G. Gibson Gallery, Jan Kesner, Charles A. Hartman, Michael Dawson, Andrew Smith TARTT/washington, Weston Gallery, Charles Isaacs, Gitterman Gallery, Edwynn Houk, Richard Moore, Ezra Mack, Silverstein Photography

Ans Westra   McNamara Gallery

Jo Whaley   Robert Koch, Lisa Sette

Robert Whitaker   Josef Lebovic

Clarence H. White   William L. Schaeffer, Keith de Lellis, Paul M. Hertzmann, Wach Gallery, Robert Koch, Janet Lehr, Contemporary / Vintage Works, Richard Moore, Lee Gallery, Silverstein Photography

Henry White   Robert Hershkowitz

John Claude White   Ken & Jenny Jacobson

Minor White   Paul M. Hertzmann, Scott Nichols, Wach Gallery, William L. Schaeffer, Etherton Gallery, Howard Greenberg, Scheinbaum & Russek, Alan Klotz, Stephen Daiter, Janet Lehr, Robert Mann, Joseph Bellows, Charles A. Hartman, TARTT/washington, G. Gibson Gallery, Gitterman Gallery, Halsted Gallery, Richard Moore, Silverstein Photography

Gordon Whitten   Etherton Gallery

Terry Wild   Joseph Bellows

Stephen Wilkes   David Gallery

John Williams   Byron McMahon

Rick Williams   Stephen L. Clark

Bob Willoughby   Staley+Wise, Keith de Lellis, David Gallery

Laura Wilson   Stephen L. Clark

Nancy Wilson-Pajic   Françoise Paviot

Wong Wayne Wilson   McNamara Gallery

John Wimberley   Michael Shapiro, John Cleary

Fonville Winans   A Gallery

Ludwig Windstosser   Photo ART

Dan Winters   Jan Kesner

Geoff Winningham   Stephen L. Clark

Garry Winogrand   Henry Feldstein, Fraenkel Gallery, Pace/MacGill, Lee Marks, Paul Kopeikin, Deborah Bell, Hyperion Press, Fahey/Klein, Jan Kesner, Zabriskie Gallery, Richard T. Rosenthal, Charles A. Hartman, Silverstein Photography

Neil Winokur   Janet Borden

Stanislaw Ignacy Witkiewicz   Robert Miller

Joel-Peter Witkin   Etherton Gallery, Picture Photo Space, Baudoin Lebon, Fahey/Klein, Catherine Edelman, HASTED HUNT, Wessel+O'Connor, Photology, Contemporary / Vintage Works, Ezra Mack, Silverstein Photography

Bill Witt   Stephen Cohen

Bill Wittliff   Photographs Do Not Bend, Stephen L. Clark

Marion Post Wolcott   Kathleen Ewing, John Cleary, Halsted Gallery, Michael Shapiro, G. Gibson Gallery, Paul Kopeikin, A Gallery, Paul M. Hertzmann, Charles A. Hartman

Michael Wolf   Robert Koch

Silvio Wolfe   Robert Mann

Annette Wolff   argus-fotokunst

Paul Wolff   argus-fotokunst, Gallery 19/21, Galerie 1900/2000

Jeffrey Wolin   Catherine Edelman

WOLS [Wolfgang Schulze]   Lee Marks, Françoise Paviot, Galerie 1900/2000

Josef Wondrak   Richard T. Rosenthal

Charles Wong   Paul M. Hertzmann, Gitterman Gallery

Seung Woo Back   RoseGallery

Woodbury & Page   Ken & Jenny Jacobson

C. D. Woolley   Stephen Bulger

Christopher Woodcock   Bonni Benrubi

Janet Woodcock   Candace Dwan

Francesca Woodman   Gary Edwards, TARTT/washington

Dawn Woodley   Stephen Bulger

John Woolf   Robert Burge

Paul Woolf   Keith de Lellis

Willard E. Worden   Richard Moore

World War II Photographs   Richard T. Rosenthal

Thomas Wrede   Paul Kopeikin

Wang Wusheng   Barry Friedman Ltd., Robert Klein

Ulrich Wüst   argus-fotokunst

Ida Wyman   Stephen Cohen

XYZ

Monsieur X Steven Kasher

Reid Yalom Candace Dwan

Masao Yamamoto Yancey Richardson, HackelBury,
Jackson Fine Art, Robert Klein, Gallery 19/21

Mariana Yampolsky Charles Schwartz,
Throckmorton Fine Art

John Yang John Stevenson

Takashi Yasumura Yossi Milo

Max Yavno Jan Kesner, Henry Feldstein, Michael
Dawson, Paul M. Hertzmann, Richard Moore

Dmitris Yeros John Stevenson

Torrance York Wm. Floyd

Kohei Yoshiyuki Yossi Milo

Anne Zahalka Robert Klein

Firooz Zahedi Staley+Wise

Robert Zahornicky Johannes Faber

Harold Zegart Paul M. Hertzmann

Jody Zellen Paul Kopeikin

Georgy Zelma Robert Koch, Nailya Alexander

Liu Zheng Yossi Milo

Alexander Zhitomirsky Gary Edwards,
Nailya Alexander

Count Zichy Richard T. Rosenthal

Willy Zielke michèle chomette

George Zimbel John Cleary, Stephen Bulger

Carl Zimmerman Stephen Bulger

Zoë Zimmerman John Stevenson

Fred Zinneman Peter Fetterman

Joe Ziolkowski Catherine Edelman

Steef Zoetmulder Paul M. Hertzmann,
Halsted Gallery

Rene Zuber Zabriskie Gallery

Guillaume Zuili Gallery 19/21

Ion Zupcu John Cleary, Halsted Gallery

René Zürcher Zur Stockeregg

Jane Zusters McNamara Gallery

Piet Zwart Michael Senft, michèle chomette

Kim Zwarts Jan Kesner